McDougal Littell

Math*Thematics*

Teacher's Resource Book

MODULE 1 Amazing Feats and Facts

MODULE 2 At the Mall

BOOK **3**

McDougal Littell

A DIVISION OF HOUGHTON MIFFLIN COMPANY

Evanston, Illinois • Boston • Dallas

Acknowledgments

Writers

The authors of *Math Thematics, Books 1–3*, wish to thank the following writers for their contributions to the *Teacher's Resource Books* for the *Math Thematics* program: **Lyle Anderson, Mary Buck, Roslyn Denny, Jean Howard, Deb Johnson, Sallie Morse, Patrick Runkel, Thomas Sanders-Garrett, Bonnie Spence, Christine Tuckerman.**

Image Credits

Photography
Front Cover © Photodisc.

Illustration
2-41, 2-44 Robin Storesund/McDougal Littell/Houghton Mifflin Co.

All other art by McDougal Littell/Houghton Mifflin Co.

THE STEM PROJECT *McDougal Littell Math Thematics*® is based on the field-test versions of The STEM Project curriculum. The STEM Project was supported in part by the

 NATIONAL SCIENCE FOUNDATION

under Grant No. ESI-0137682. Opinions expressed in *McDougal Littell Math Thematics*® are those of the authors and not necessarily those of the National Science Foundation.

ISBN-13: 978-0-547-00117-3
ISBN-10: 0-547-00117-7

123456789–BHV–11 10 09 08 07

Contents

About the Teacher's Resource Book

In conjunction with the *Math Thematics*, Book 3, Teacher's Edition, this Resource Book contains all of the teaching support that you need to teach Modules 1 and 2.

Math Thematics Overview

The first Resource Book for each level includes the following course overview materials:

Teaching with *Math Thematics* A detailed explanation of the sections in the student textbook, the planning support in the Teacher's Edition, and the teaching resources in the Teacher's Resource Books.

Assessment in *Math Thematics* A description of the various forms of assessment available to the teacher in the student textbook, in the Teacher's Edition, and in the Teacher's Resource Books. Includes a detailed discussion of the use of Assessment Scales in this program, and suggestions for creating portfolios.

Teacher's Scavenger Hunt A scavenger hunt through the *Math Thematics* program's components to help teachers become more familiar with all the resources available to them.

Literature Connections A list of literature excerpts used in *Math Thematics*, Book 3.

Materials List A list of materials needed for use with Labsheets, Explorations, and Exercises in *Math Thematics*, Book 3.

Blackline Masters

The teaching support in the Resource Books is organized by module and section and includes the following materials:

Warm-Up Exercises Each Warm-Up page is printed in large easy-to-read type and can be used to create an overhead visual or used as a hand-out. Answers for the exercises are provided at the bottom of the page.

Labsheets Blackline masters used in conjunction with various Exploration questions to present data and extend the scope of the Exploration. Answers are provided in the Teacher's Edition.

Practice and Applications One to two pages of additional practice for each section in a module, as well as combined practice that covers the whole module.

Study Guide Two to three pages of Study Guide for each section of the module. These Study Guide pages feature key concepts, worked-out examples, and exercises. They can be used for review and reteaching.

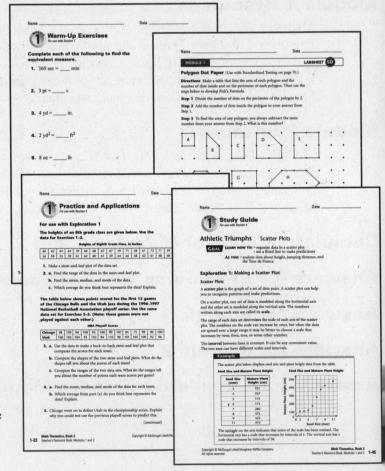

Extended Exploration (E²) Solution Guide

A comprehensive discussion of the Extended Exploration in the student textbook, including how to assess student responses and performance.

Alternate Extended Exploration (Alternate E²)

Included in the Teacher's Resource Books for Modules 2, 4, 6, and 7, these extended explorations can be substituted for ones in the student textbook. Materials include teaching notes and assessment procedures.

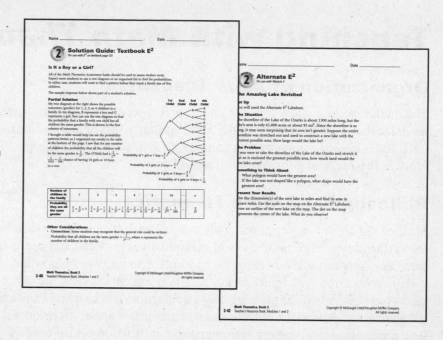

Assessment

Assessment options include a diagnostic module pre-test, quick quizzes for each section, a mid-module quiz, and two module tests, Forms A and B.

Cumulative Test

A cumulative test on both the modules of this Resource Book.

Module Standardized Test

A page of standardized multiple-choice questions for each module.

Module Performance Assessment

A Performance Assessment Task for each module.

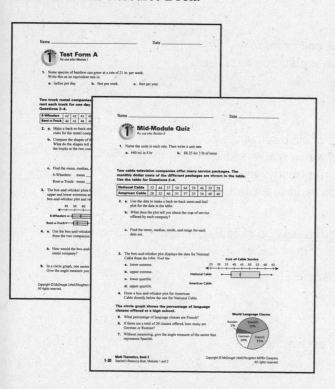

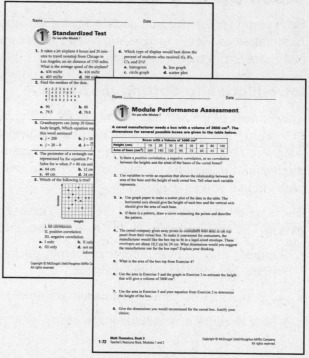

Answers

Complete answers to Practice and Applications, Study Guide, Quick Quizzes, and all Assessments for both modules are provided at the back of this Resource Book.

Teaching with *Math Thematics*

Organization of *Math Thematics*

The mathematics content for each grade level is presented in eight thematic modules that connect the mathematical ideas to real-world applications. Each module contains four to six sections, an *Extended Exploration*, a *Module Project*, and a *Review and Assessment*.

Philosophy of *Math Thematics*

Most of the *Math Thematics* materials are written so that students discover the mathematics. Through the use of manipulatives, models, and hands-on activities, students actively learn the concepts. The rules and algorithms usually associated with mathematics are often student-derived, rather than given in the text. Explaining why an algorithm works helps students internalize the procedure. Because some concepts or applications do not lend themselves to discovery learning, direct instruction is also used in *Math Thematics*.

It will be important for you, as a teacher, to work through many of the questions in the Explorations and Exercises. Because of the interactive nature of this curriculum, it is important for teachers to be aware of the possible questions their students might ask and of the problems they might encounter.

Close-Up of a Section

Each section is divided into parts: a *Setting the Stage*, one or more Explorations, a Key Concepts summary, Practice and Application Exercises, and Extra Skill Practice, as described below.

Introduction to *Setting the Stage*

The purpose of the *Setting the Stage* at the beginning of each section is to capture students' interest and relate the mathematics to a real-world situation. This is an integral part of a section because it provides the motivation for learning the mathematics of the section or introduces a problem that will be explored.

There are three types of *Setting the Stage*. These sections may be a reading passage, an activity, a visual display, or some combination of these.

- Readings may include literature excerpts, poems, stories, or articles written for a middle school audience.

- Activities may be games, simulations, or quizzes.

- Visual displays may include maps, charts, graphs, or diagrams.

Each *Setting the Stage* includes *Think About It* questions, which help deepen the student's understanding of what he or she has read, done, or seen. The questions range from simple recall to application. Often, students intuitively explore an idea in the *Think About It* questions that they will later investigate in depth.

Introduction to an Exploration

After the *Setting the Stage*, each section contains one to three Explorations where students are actively involved in learning new mathematical content. Each Exploration requires one class period, and, depending on the nature of the activity, may be completed by students working individually, in small groups, or as a whole class. The activities in the Explorations range from guided discovery to open-ended investigations. Students investigate a question or problem by doing one or more of the following:

- Collecting, generating, researching, and presenting data
- Using concrete and/or visual models
- Applying problem solving strategies
- Looking for patterns and relationships
- Exploring alternative methods and solutions
- Using number sense
- Applying prior knowledge.

The Explorations provide opportunities for students to observe, analyze, predict, make and test conjectures, and communicate their ideas orally and in writing.

Goals, *Key Terms*, and *Set Up*

Each Exploration and some *Setting the Stage* sections begin with a *Goal* and may include a list of *Key Terms* and a *Set Up*, if appropriate.

- The Goal statements give a summary of the mathematics being covered.

- The Key Terms list important vocabulary being introduced in the Exploration and can serve as an advanced organizer for students who need it.

- Both students and teachers should read the Set Up, which lists the most appropriate class set up—whole class, small groups, or individual—as well as any materials needed for the activity. The materials listed may include Labsheets, which are used in conjunction with various Exploration questions to present data and extend the scope of the Exploration. The Labsheets are available in the Teacher's Resource Books (as blackline masters) and in the Student Workbook. Labsheets may also be used with many exercises, and with the Extended Explorations, Module Project, and Review and Assessment pages.

Exploration Questions

Communicating about and through mathematics, both orally and in writing, is embedded throughout the *Math Thematics* curriculum.

- Discussion questions provide opportunities for students to check their understanding of a concept by sharing or generating ideas with others. The questions can be explored in pairs, in groups of four, or as a class.

- Try This as a Class questions are designed to bring the class together to develop an algorithm, pull ideas together, pool data, or complete a more challenging problem.

- Checkpoint questions are provided as a way to quickly assess whether students understand the mathematics.

Student Support Notes

- Side notes accompany Checkpoints to remind students what they have been learning.

- Each Exploration concludes with a list of Homework Exercises related to the content of that Exploration.

- For Help boxes in Explorations and elsewhere refer students to the module where a concept was first learned or to the Toolbox or Tables at the back of the textbook.

Introduction to *Key Concepts*

Students can use the *Key Concepts* to review for a test or as a reference when they have missed a day of class. The *Key Concepts* are also a resource for parents who are helping their child with homework.

Key Concept pages can be helpful in the following ways:

- Giving a quick overview of content
- Illustrating the content with examples
- Highlighting the most important content
- Listing the new vocabulary in the section, and
- Providing a reference to applicable pages in the Exploration.

The *Key Concept Question* reinforces the ideas from the section, often pulling the content of all the Explorations in the section together.

Introduction to *Practice and Application Exercises*

The questions in the *Practice and Application Exercises* include skill level, application, single-answer, open-ended, and critical thinking questions. A wide variety of topics are covered in these exercises. Students may explore how the content relates to other areas of mathematics, other subjects, or different cultures.

- The Teacher's Edition provides a guide to using many of these exercises as embedded assessment items.

- The Reflecting on the Section questions can also be used to assess student learning.

- The Spiral Review exercises revisit topics from previous sections in the module as well as concepts from previous modules. They may also review material mastered at a prior grade level. They are carefully planned to provide an ongoing schedule of practice to help students master content and prepare students for upcoming sections by reviewing prerequisite skills.

Some sections may include these questions:

- A Career Connection, a set of application-based exercises about people who use mathematics in their career

- Extension problems that challenge students to extend what they have learned and apply it in a new setting.

Introduction to *Extra Skill Practice*

The first half of the *Extra Skill Practice* reinforces the concepts students investigated in the Explorations of the section. The exercises are usually at a skill level but sometimes are application-based.

The bottom half of the page focuses on *Study Skills* in some sections and *Standardized Testing* in other sections.

- Study Skills questions explore how students learn (visual, auditory, or kinesthetic), how to take notes, and how the text is organized.

- Standardized Testing questions help students become comfortable with various formats of standardized testing questions using the mathematical content of the section.

Organization of the *Teacher's Edition*

The *Teacher's Edition* provides suggestions at *point of use* for helping students understand new concepts and avoid common errors. Other features include classroom examples, classroom management ideas, and ideas for differentiating instruction.

Complete planning support is provided by module and section planning guides that include mathematical overviews and teaching strategies, day-by-day planning guides, and suggested homework assignments. The *Teacher's Edition* also includes professional articles and resources available for each section, including technology resources. See the *Teacher's Edition*, pages T35 and T36–T47.

Organization of the *Teacher's Resource Books*

Teaching resources are presented in four *Teacher's Resource Books* at each grade level, with each Resource Book containing materials for two modules. These resources are organized by section to make it easy for teachers to find the materials available for that section. The *Teacher's Resource Books* contain a variety of resources for each module:

- Teaching tools, including section warm-up exercises, labsheets, additional practice and application exercises, study guide materials, and parent newsletters

- Assessment tools, including section and mid-module quizzes, module diagnostic pre-tests, module tests, standardized tests, module performance assessments, cumulative tests, and pre-course, mid-year, and end-of-year tests

- Answers, including answers for all Resource Book materials for the two modules and any cumulative tests in that Resource Book.

See the descriptions of each of these resource types on pages TR-4 and TR-5 in this *Teacher's Resource Book for Modules 1 and 2*.

The information on pages TR-11–TR-25 describes the Assessment component in the *Math Thematics* program. After reviewing these materials, you may want to take the Teacher's Scavenger Hunt on pages TR-26 and TR-27 to help you become more familiar with how to use all the components of the *Math Thematics*, Book 3 program. (Answers are provided.)

Assessment in *Math Thematics*

Introduction

Assessment, by which we mean all the procedures used to collect information on any aspect of the teaching and learning process, is an integral component of the *Math Thematics* curriculum.

The assessment component in *Math Thematics* provides a guidance system—a guidance system for teachers, for parents, and most importantly, for students.

Purposes of Assessment

The primary purpose of assessment is to improve learning. To achieve this goal, the *Math Thematics* assessment component is designed to be an integral part of the instructional process, rather than an add-on to it. Not only is assessment information drawn from instructional tasks, but the assessment tools themselves are designed to help students master concepts and develop skills.

The *Math Thematics* assessment component serves four major purposes:

- Monitoring student progress in problem solving, reasoning, and communication

A major goal of the *Math Thematics* curriculum is to develop each student's ability to solve problems, reason logically, and communicate ideas effectively. Making problem solving, reasoning, and communication a primary focus of assessment conveys the message that these are valued skills. But more importantly, the scales used for *Teacher Assessment* and *Student Self-Assessment* provide dynamic tools for helping students learn what they can do to improve in these areas.

- Assessing student proficiency in content areas

Assessment data are used to document students' understanding of mathematical content and processes, and to determine whether students have achieved the learner outcomes of the *Math Thematics* curriculum. The data are derived from multiple sources using a broad range of mathematical tasks.

- Helping teachers make instructional decisions

The assessment tools provide information teachers can use to decide what instruction is necessary to help students achieve the outcomes of the *Math Thematics* curriculum. The results of ongoing assessment may indicate a variety of needs such as reteaching concepts, reviewing or practicing skills, or presenting additional material using a different model or teaching technique.

- Documenting student progress for students, parents, and teachers

Assessment is about more than grades, but teachers are usually expected to translate assessment data into grades. Samples of student work gathered during assessment can provide an objective basis for determining student performance levels. Having a portfolio containing examples of a student's work can show growth over time. By comparing examples in the portfolio, you can clearly communicate to the student, parents, and other teachers the indicators of excellent work (A), good progress (B), developing concepts and skills (C), and minimally acceptable work (D).

Assessment Tools

The following assessment tools are incorporated into the *Math Thematics* curriculum. (See also the Summary of Assessment on pages T30–T31 in the *Teacher's Edition*.)

Warm-Ups

Warm-Ups are short activities found in the *Teacher's Resource Books* that provide systematic review of concepts and skills. *Warm-Ups* can be photocopied for the class or projected with an overhead. They are often used for pre-assessment purposes to determine whether students have the prerequisite skills or knowledge for a section.

Embedded Questions

Because assessment in *Math Thematics* is an integral part of instruction, many assessment items are embedded in the instructional materials.

Discussion questions provide opportunities for students to check their understanding of a concept by sharing or generating ideas within their group or as a class. Mastery of the concept is not expected at this point, but teachers should monitor the discussions to check for misconceptions that may need to be corrected.

Checkpoints are questions or problems that are used by the teacher to check understanding of a concept or skill before students continue with the exploration. *Checkpoints* appear after students have explored a concept and when some level of mastery is expected. If students are not able to complete the problems correctly, re-teaching may be necessary.

Try This as a Class questions appear at points where direct instruction is needed to summarize key ideas or to bring closure to a line of inquiry. They are similar to *Discussion* questions, except that the teacher directs the discussion or activity and guides the learning. Not all *Try This as a Class* questions are used for assessment. Some are simply used to demonstrate a procedure or to pool data.

Some *Practice & Application Exercises* are designed to be used to assess whether students have learned specific concepts, procedures, and processes. These exercises, which may be used for instructional decision making and grading, are identified in the *Teacher's Edition* as embedded assessment exercises. They range from straightforward applications of concepts and procedures to open-ended questions that require students to recognize the appropriate mathematical content, choose an effective approach, and construct a response.

Reflecting on the Section exercises provide an opportunity for students to look back on the section as a whole and refine, describe, summarize, or extend the mathematical ideas they have explored. A *Reflecting* exercise may take the form of a *Discussion, Research, Oral Report, Journal,* or *Visual Thinking* question. Writing or talking about a concept helps students solidify their understanding of it. It may also help them make connec-

tions to other subject areas or among mathematical concepts. Students' responses to the *Reflecting* exercises should be considered for inclusion in their portfolios.

Extended Explorations (E²s)

E^2s are extended problem solving activities. They are typically open-ended problems that apply a variety of mathematical concepts and may be solved in different ways. The solution often involves constructing a mathematical model for the situation. To solve the problem, students must define the problem, devise and carry out a plan for solving it, and prepare a presentation in which they explain and interpret their solution. Each E^2 may be assigned for completion in about a week's time. The solution is assessed using the *Teacher Assessment Scales* and *Student Self-Assessment Scales*. Solutions to some E^2s should be included in students' portfolios to document growth in problem solving, reasoning, and communication.

A sample Solution Guide for the textbook E^2 is provided in the *Teacher's Resource Book* for each module. In addition, Alternate Extended Explorations and their solutions are provided in the *Teacher's Resource Books* for Modules 2, 4, 6, and 7.

(For more information on *Managing Extended Explorations*, see the article on pages T44–T45 in the *Teacher's Edition*. For help with assessing E^2 solutions, see the Format for an E^2 Solution, sample Scoring Profiles, and sample Student Solutions materials on pages 1-60 to 1-63 in this *Teacher's Resource Book for Module 1*.)

Module Projects

Each module contains a *Module Project* that provides an opportunity for students to apply mathematical concepts as they learn them. The project is related to the theme of the module, but may also require mathematical knowledge from earlier modules. Questions and activities in the *Module Project* relate to the mathematical concepts taught in the module. Students prepare a report or presentation to complete the project. Some *Module Projects* should be included in students' portfolios to demonstrate their understanding of mathematical concepts as well their ability to apply them.

Module Review and Assessment

Each module concludes with a set of questions that can be used to review and assess the content of the module. Additional assessment materials are provided in each of the *Teacher's Resource Books*. These include mid-module quizzes, module tests, Standardized Tests and Module Performance Assessments.

Portfolios

A student portfolio is a collection of representative samples of the student's work. It may include such things as assignments, answers to *Reflecting on the Section* exercises, solutions to and *Module Projects*. Its purpose is to provide comprehensive documentation of the student's progress in, attitude toward, and understanding of mathematics over a period of time.

Using the *Math Thematics Assessment Scales*

About the *Math Thematics Assessment Scales*

The *Math Thematics Assessment Scales* are designed to help students answer the question "How can I improve my performance in problem solving, reasoning, and communications?" They provide a generalized rubric that defines the various dimensions of mathematical investigation. The scales are designed to be applied to open-ended questions, *Module Projects, Reflecting on the Section* exercises, and especially *Extended Explorations (E²s)*. Students are encouraged to write their solutions to these items using appropriate mathematical language and representations to communicate how they solved the problem, the decisions they made as they solved it, and any connections they made. Their work is assessed using five scales:

- Problem Solving
- Mathematical Language
- Representations
- Connections
- Presentation

The key to improving student performance is to actively involve them in assessing their own work. This is achieved through use of the *Student Self-Assessment Scales*. As students become familiar with the scales, they understand what they need to do to improve their problem solving, reasoning, and communication.

Teachers assess students' work using the same scales written from a teacher's point of view. The combination of student and teacher assessment provides important feedback to help students improve.

If used consistently, the *Math Thematics Assessment Scales* have the potential to raise the level of students' performance. However, you and your students will not master the use of the *Math Thematics Assessment Scales* immediately. This is okay—the more work you and your students assess, the better and the more comfortable you will be with the assessment process.

As you work with the *Math Thematics Assessment Scales*, keep the following in mind:

- The scales are a powerful way for both you and your students to look at work.
- Learning to use the scales is like learning a new language. It requires time and patience.
- Students' higher-order thinking skills will improve as a result of using the *Math Thematics Assessment Scales*.
- Be flexible!

A copy of all the scales can be found on page 1-6 (*Teacher Assessment Scales*) and on page 1-7 (*Student Self-Assessment Scales*) in this *Teacher's Resource Book*. The scales are repeated in the Resource Book for each module. The *Student Self-Assessment Scales* also appear on page 599 in the student textbook.

The following are descriptions of each scale.

The Problem Solving Scale

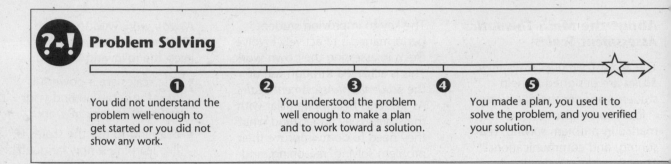

Problem Solving

① You did not understand the problem well enough to get started or you did not show any work.

② ③ You understood the problem well enough to make a plan and to work toward a solution.

④ ⑤ You made a plan, you used it to solve the problem, and you verified your solution.

The *Problem Solving Scale* assesses the student's ability to select and use appropriate mathematical concepts and problem solving strategies (guess and check, make a model, look for a pattern, and so on) to solve a problem. The scale emphasizes and reinforces the steps in the *4-Step Approach to Solving Problems*—Understand the Problem, Make a Plan, Carry Out the Plan, and Look Back.

The *Teacher Assessment Scale* shown above gives the range of the criteria used to assess a student's work for problem solving. The following descriptions expand on the criteria.

Level 5: The student's approach worked and led to a correct solution.

The following are characteristics of a Level 5 solution:

- All the relevant information was used to solve the problem.
- The problem solving strategies, procedures, and mathematical concepts used were appropriate for the problem and were carried out completely.

- When strategies were only partially useful, the approach was modified successfully.
- The solution was checked for reasonableness.
- Other possible solutions were explored.
- The solution was verified through the use of a second approach or with a clear explanation of how the approach actually solved the problem.

Level 3: The student was able to make progress toward a solution.

The following are characteristics of a Level 3 solution:

- A workable plan was used, but the solution is incomplete or only solves part of the problem.
- The problem was only partially solved because some of the relevant data were not used.
- The mathematical procedures and problem solving strategies used were appropriate for the problem, but they were not carried out completely or they did not lead to a complete solution.

- The mathematical concepts chosen were appropriate but only partially solved the problem.

Level 1: The student did not understand the problem well enough to get started on a solution or did not show any work.

The following are characteristics of a Level 1 solution:

- There was no apparent plan for solving the problem or solution was not related to the problem.
- Information was misinterpreted or irrelevant data was used.
- Problem solving strategies were used randomly or were not used at all.
- Incorrect or inappropriate mathematical procedures were used.
- The mathematical concepts chosen were not appropriate for the problem.

Levels 2 and 4 may be used to show performance that falls between the described levels. For example, a student may have used an appropriate approach and found a correct solution to the problem, but then stopped without checking the reasonableness of the solution or trying to verify it. This solution might be scored at Level 4 rather than Level 5. Similarly, a solution that has some of the characteristics of a Level 1 solution and some of a Level 3 solution might be scored at Level 2. The Star (☆) Level should only be used to indicate exceptional work.

The score on a scale is shown by filling it in with a marker up to the level number.

Questions Students Ask About the *Problem Solving Scale*

What is meant by a solution?

A solution includes your answer and all the work you did to get it. Sometimes it may be necessary to include an explanation of your approach and why you chose it.

What if I make a computation error? How does that affect my score?

The goal in problem solving is always to find an accurate solution, so you should make it a habit to check your work carefully. It is still possible, however, to get an incorrect answer because of a minor computational error. Depending on how serious the error is, this may lower your score one level on the *Problem Solving Scale*. The error will be noted at the bottom of the assessment sheet.

What does it mean to "verify my solution"?

The most common way to verify a solution is to solve it another way. For example, you could solve the problem using different problem solving strategies or a different approach and show that you get the same answer. Another way to verify your solution is by clearly explaining your plan and showing that it effectively solved the problem.

The Mathematical Language Scale

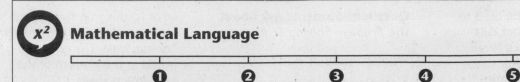

x² Mathematical Language

1 You did not use any mathematical vocabulary or symbols, or you did not use them correctly, or your use was not appropriate.

2

3 You used appropriate mathematical language, but the way it was used was not always correct or other terms and symbols were needed.

4

5 You used mathematical language that was correct and appropriate to make your meaning clear.

The *Mathematical Language Scale* assesses the student's use of mathematical vocabulary, notation, and symbols. The scale encourages consistent and accurate use of mathematical language.

Level 5: The student used mathematical language correctly and consistently. The language used was appropriate for the problem and it helped to simplify or clarify the solution.

The following are characteristics of a Level 5 solution:

- The mathematical language used was appropriate for the problem.

- The mathematical vocabulary and symbols were used consistently and accurately.

- The use of mathematical terms and symbols helped to communicate the solution.

Level 3: The student used appropriate mathematical vocabulary and symbols, but the usage was not always correct or additional terms and symbols could have been used to simplify the solution or make it clearer.

The following are characteristics of a Level 3 solution:

- The mathematical vocabulary and symbols chosen were appropriate for the problem but more could have been used.

- Appropriate mathematical terms and symbols were used, but they were not used consistently or there were minor errors in usage.

Level 1: The student did not use mathematical vocabulary or notation in the solution, or the terms and symbols used were inappropriate or used incorrectly.

The following are characteristics of a Level 1 solution:

- The use of mathematical terms and symbols the student should know would have helped to simplify or to clarify the solution, but none were used.

- Inappropriate mathematical language was used.

- Mathematical terms or symbols were used incorrectly or imprecisely.

Questions Students Ask About the *Mathematical Language Scale*

What is appropriate mathemat[ical] language?

You are using appropriate ma[th]ematical language if the term[s] and symbols you are using he[lp] to simplify your solution or to make it clearer. Using extrane[ous] terms or symbols that do not relate to the problem or aid i[n] the solution is inappropriate.

Does one mistake in language lower my score?

Usually, one error would not lower your score, especially if the other terms and symbols you used were appropriate a[nd] were used correctly.

The Representations Scale

 Representations

① You did not use any representations such as equations, tables, graphs, or diagrams to help solve the problem or explain your solution.

②

③ You made appropriate representations to help solve the problem or help you explain your solution, but they were not always correct or other representations were needed.

④

⑤ You used appropriate and correct representations to solve the problem or explain your solution.

The *Representations Scale* assesses the student's use of graphs, tables, models, diagrams, and equations to solve problems. The *Representations Scale* looks specifically at whether the representations are accurate and appropriate.

Level 5: The student used representations that were accurate and appropriate for the problem. The representations helped to solve the problem or explain the solution.

The following are characteristics of a Level 5 solution:

- The representations used were appropriate for the problem.

- The representations helped to solve the problem or to communicate the solution.

- The representations were correct and accurate.

Level 3: The student used representations that were appropriate for the problem, but they were not always accurate or correct, and other representations could have been used to simplify the solution or to make it clearer.

The following are characteristics of a Level 3 solution:

- The representations used were appropriate for the problem, but additional representations were needed to solve the problem or to help communicate the solution.

- The representations were appropriate, but there were some errors in constructing or using the representations.

Level 1: The student did not use representations to help solve the problem or to explain the solution.

The following are characteristics of a Level 1 solution:

- The use of representations would have helped solve the problem or clarify the solution, but none were used.

- The representations used were inappropriate for the problem and did not help solve it or explain the solution.

Questions Students Ask About the *Representations Scale*

What makes a representation appropriate?

To be appropriate, a representation must accurately represent relevant information in the problem or help to organize the information. The representation should actually solve or help to solve the problem. For example, suppose the data in a problem could be displayed in a circle graph, but the graph does not solve the problem or give you a clue about how to solve it. Then it is inappropriate.

What makes a representation accurate?

A graph is accurate if the axes are labeled, the graph displays data that are relevant to the problem, the data are plotted accurately, the graph is titled correctly, and, if necessary, an accurate key is provided. A table, chart, diagram, or model is accurate if it is correctly labeled, it is well organized, and it accurately reflects information relevant to the problem.

The Connections Scale

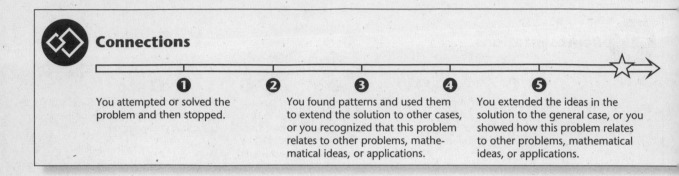

Connections

❶ You attempted or solved the problem and then stopped.

❸ You found patterns and used them to extend the solution to other cases, or you recognized that this problem relates to other problems, mathematical ideas, or applications.

❺ You extended the ideas in the solution to the general case, or you showed how this problem relates to other problems, mathematical ideas, or applications.

The *Connections Scale* assesses the student's ability to make connections within mathematics, to real-world situations, and to other disciplines. This scale emphasizes and reinforces the Look Back step in the *4-Step Approach to Solving Problems.*

This is the most difficult scale for students to understand and use. Because they often have limited mathematical knowledge and virtually no experience making connections, students' initial connections will be limited to recalling similar problems, finding and extending patterns, and relating the math to their everyday lives. To help students grow in this area, it is extremely important to continually encourage them and prompt them to look for and to make connections.

When extending solutions to the general case, many students lack the skills to express the general rule algebraically. Their extensions will involve descriptions of the patterns they found and may include a verbal rule. This is particularly true for sixth grade students. As students mature, their ability to use algebraic notation should increase, and they should become comfortable using it.

Level 5: The student generalized the solution or showed how the problem is related to other problems, mathematical ideas, or applications.

The following are characteristics of a Level 5 solution:

- The solution was extended to the general case.

- The solution was applied or interpreted in a real-world situation.

- The student clearly demonstrated how the problem is related to another mathematical concept or to another problem.

Level 3: The student recognized patterns and was able to use them to extend the solution to other cases of the same problem or recognized that the problem is related to other mathematical ideas, problems, or applications.

The following are characteristics of a Level 3 solution:

- The student found patterns that led to the solution but did not generalize the solution.

- The solution was extended to other cases of the same problem.

- Alternative solutions were explored.

- The student recognized that the problem is related to other problems, mathematical concepts, or applications but did not explain or illustrate the connection.

Level 1: The student solved the problem and stopped without looking back to see how the solution might be extended or generalized or how the problem relates to other problems, content, or applications.

The following are characteristics of a Level 1 solution:

- There are connections that the student should have recognized, but none were mentioned or explained in the solution.

- The solution does not indicate that the student looked for patterns that might be generalized.

- Alternative solutions were not recognized or were not pursued.

- The problem was not checked or examined from a different perspective.

Questions Students Ask About the *Connections Scale*

What does it mean to extend my solution?

After you have solved a problem, you can extend it in many ways. One way is to solve the problem for different cases. For example, suppose a problem asked you to find the number of handshakes that would occur when five people shook hands exactly once. If you solved the problem for five people and then found the number of handshakes for six, seven, and eight people too, you have extended the solution. Another way to extend a problem is to write a general rule that can be used to find the number of handshakes for any number of people.

In Levels 3 and 5 on the Connections Scale, *what is the difference between recognizing that the problem relates to other problems, mathematical ideas, or applications and showing that it does?*

When you first begin making connections, you will discover that problems are related to other problems, mathematics, or applications. You might say "this is just like the handshake problem." In this case, you recognized the connection. When you show the connection, you will clearly link the problem, mathematics, or application with an explanation.

The Presentation Scale

Presentation

❶   ❷   ❸   ❹   ❺   ☆→

❶ The presentation of your solution and reasoning is unclear to others.

❸ The presentation of your solution and reasoning is clear in most places, but others may have trouble understanding parts of it.

❺ The presentation of your solution and reasoning is clear and can be understood by others.

The *Presentation Scale* assesses the student's ability to reason logically and to communicate ideas effectively. This scale assesses why students did what they did to solve the problem. Evidence of reasoning is shown by making and testing conjectures, formulating models, explaining why, and gathering and presenting evidence. The differences between levels on the scale reflect both the correctness and the clarity of reasoning.

Level 5: The presentation clearly explains what the student did, why it was done, and how it solved the problem.

The following are characteristics of a Level 5 solution:

• The student's work was clear and focused. The details presented fit together and made sense.

• The presentation was well organized. One step followed from another.

• Strong supporting arguments were presented.

• All the important aspects of the problem and the relevant data were identified.

• Examples and counterexamples were included where appropriate.

• The solution is such that anyone who reads it will follow what was done, why it was done, and how the solution was obtained.

Level 3: The presentation explains what the student did and why it was done, but parts of the explanation are incorrect or are not clear.

The following are characteristics of a Level 3 solution:

• There is either an explanation or a clear inference of appropriate reasoning in the solution.

• Almost all of the reasoning is correct, but some of it may be unclear.

• There is evidence that unsuitable methods and incorrect solutions were eliminated.

Level 1: The presentation does not clearly explain or demonstrate what the student did or why it was done.

The following are characteristics of a Level 1 solution:

• The solution does not solve the question that was asked.

• There is no evidence of reasoned decision-making in the solution, or the solution indicates the possibility of reasoned decision-making, but the reader cannot be sure.

• The solution was organized in a haphazard or disjointed manner.

• The reasoning was incorrect.

• The solution does not contain an explanation of what was done and why, or the explanation is not understandable.

Questions Students Ask About the *Presentation Scale*

What does it mean to clearly explain my reasoning?

You must explain how you arrived at your solution and why you took each step you did. For example, if a student joined our class today and read your solution, would that student understand what you did and why you did it?

Do I always have to tell in words why I did what I did in order to score high on this scale?

It is possible that your work is organized so clearly that your reasoning can be inferred. However, it is helpful for you to explain what you did and why you did it. Some people think more clearly when they write things out, so writing helps them to clarify the situation and their thoughts.

About the *Math Thematics Assessment Scales*

Questions Teachers Ask About the *Assessment Scales*

What if the student and I do not agree on the assessment?

This is an excellent opportunity to discuss the differences between the assessments with the student. Comparing and contrasting the teacher and student assessments provides an important feedback loop that will lead to improved problem solving, reasoning, and communication.

Can the Math Thematics *Assessment Scales be used to assess problems that were solved as a group?*

Yes. Individual accountability is very important to the success of cooperative learning. So even if students work in a group to solve a problem, they should document the work individually. This individual documentation can be assessed using the assessment scales.

How can I tell if an exercise should be assessed with the Math Thematics Assessment Scales*?*

All *Extended Explorations* should be assessed using the assessment scales. Additional exercises that can be assessed with the scales are identified in the *Teacher's Edition.*

Will all the problems allow a student to score at the highest level on each scale?

No. Some problems have greater potential for certain scales than others. Sometimes students may not even be scored on a scale because the problem does not elicit the criteria for that scale.

If a problem is not scored on a scale, how will a grade be affected?

If a problem is not scored on a scale, the scale should not be counted when assigning the grade.

What if the student doesn't use the content I expected?

When solving problems, students should be encouraged to use any concepts they know. They should not be penalized for approaching the problem in a different way than the teacher expected.

Should I score students' earlier work more easily than later work?

No. The goal is to get students to improve so you should use a consistent scoring throughout the course.

When should I use Level 2, Level 4, and the Star (☆) Level as scores?

Levels 2 and 4 may be used to show performance that falls between the described levels. For example, a student may have used an appropriate approach and found a correct solution to the problem, but then stopped without checking the reasonableness of the solution or trying to verify it. This solution might be scored at Level 4 rather than Level 5. Similarly, a solution that has some of a Level 3 solution might be scored at Level 2. The Star (☆) Level should only be used to indicate exceptional work.

Using Portfolios

Why Portfolios?

Portfolios are a means of assessing students' progress over time. They allow the teacher to focus on a student's collected work rather than on the work of all students on a single activity. Because they provide students with an opportunity for reflection and goal-setting, portfolios are valuable self-assessment tools. By providing tangible evidence of what students have achieved, portfolios help to instill a sense of pride and accomplishment in students and provide very useful tools for communicating with students, parents, and other teachers.

Creating Portfolios

The *Math Thematics* curriculum recognizes the importance of maintaining student portfolios, but understands that there is no single format that will meet the needs of all teachers and all schools using the curriculum. What follows is one possible model.

A portfolio is created cooperatively by the student and the teacher. Work selected for inclusion in the portfolio by the teacher or the student must be accompanied by a *Portfolio Entry Cover Sheet* completed by the student. The cover sheet describes why the piece was chosen, how it reflects the student's understanding of the mathematics content, and any other reflections the student may have. At any time, the student may improve the work. When the student improves a piece, the *Portfolio Entry Cover Sheet* must include what portions were changed and w the student decided to impro the piece.

To create the portfolio, the student should have two folde In one folder, the student sho keep all of the work during a grading period. The student can then look at the work and decide which pieces should b included in the portfolio. The teacher may suggest some pie es to be included. There may also be times when a teacher tells all students to include a particular piece in their portfo lios. The student is responsibl for organizing the work in the portfolio with suggestions giv by the teacher. Some suggestions on what may be include in the portfolio are given on t next page.

Organizing Your Work

Save all your work in the work folder. At any time, you may choose a piece of work to include in your portfolio. All work going into your work folder must be dated and include your name. Keep the following in your work folder:

- All tests and quizzes.
- All class work and homework assignments.
- All E²s and *Self-Assessment Forms*.
- *Module Projects*.
- Any other assignment that you needed to complete.

You may improve any piece of work you have completed. When you do, include a written description of what you improved and why you improved the work. This will be helpful if you decide to include the piece in your portfolio.

You may begin creating the actual portfolio at any time by selecting pieces you feel best reflect your work. Each piece must include a *Portfolio Entry Cover Sheet*.

Contents of a Portfolio

Your portfolio represents your work as a mathematics student. It should be something that you would be proud to show other students, teachers, and parents. It must be organized and neat. The portfolio should show the progress you make over a period of time. The following items must be included in your portfolio.

Table of Contents: The first page of your portfolio (not including the cover) should be the *Table of Contents*. The work in your portfolio should be numbered in the same order as in your *Table of Contents*.

Letter to the Reader: The *Letter to the Reader* should give a brief description of how the portfolio reflects your understanding of mathematics and brief descriptions of the pieces in the portfolio.

Self-Assessment Form: The *Self-Assessment Form* gives you the opportunity to reflect on your progress. You may also list any important goals you might have for the next grading period.

Portfolio Entry Cover Sheet: A *Portfolio Entry Cover Sheet* should accompany each piece going into your portfolio.

Work: The work included in your portfolio will vary. Individual pieces may include: *Extended Explorations (E²s)*, *Module Projects*, home or class assignments, tests and quizzes, work from a section, and *Reflecting on the Section* exercises.

Mathematical Autobiography: Your *Mathematical Autobiography* gives you the opportunity to reflect on your past mathematical experiences and attitudes. It should be completed at the beginning of the year.

Attitude Survey: In the *Attitude Survey*, you reflect on your attitudes about mathematics and what improvements could be made in the class.

Portfolio Summary: The *Portfolio Summary* should be included at the end of your portfolio. In it, you should summarize your progress. You also have the opportunity to identify particular goals you may have for the future.

Self-Assessment Form

For each of the following statements, check the response that best describes your ideas about your work in this grading period.

Problem Solving

	Usually	Sometimes	Rarely
I am able to read the problem successfully and understand what it is about.	☐	☐	☐
I am able to develop a plan and choose a strategy to solve the problem.	☐	☐	☐
I am able to apply problem solving strategies in working through the problem.	☐	☐	☐
I often look back over my work to see that I have answered the questions accurately and completely.	☐	☐	☐

Mathematical Communication

	Usually	Sometimes	Rarely
I use mathematical vocabulary in talking and writing about mathematics.	☐	☐	☐
I feel confident when reading and writing mathematical symbols.	☐	☐	☐
I regularly use and understand models, diagrams, tables, and graphs.	☐	☐	☐

Mathematical Reasoning

	Usually	Sometimes	Rarely
I am able to explain and support my thoughts and conclusions about mathematical ideas.	☐	☐	☐
I am able to understand other people's mathematical thoughts and explanations.	☐	☐	☐

Mathematical Connections

	Usually	Sometimes	Rarely
Remembering what I've already learned helps me understand new math topics.	☐	☐	☐

These are the important things I want to work on:

1.
2.
3.

Portfolio Entry Cover Sheet

I am including this in my portfolio because:

As you review this work, I hope you will notice:

(If this piece needs revision, you must explain how you would improve it and/or what the mistakes were. If you still have difficulties with the mathematics, you need to attach an explanation to this sheet.)

Math Thematics, Book 3

Name _____ Date _____

Attitude Survey

1. Name two or three of the most important or most interesting things you have learned in math class. Explain why they were interesting or important.

2. Name at least one area of mathematics with which you still need help.

3. How do you feel at this moment about math class? (Circle all that apply. If needed, fill in the blank with another adjective you feel applies.)

interested   successful   excited   happy   relaxed

confused   worried   rushed   frustrated

_____

4. Name one way you can improve math class. Also suggest one way the class as a whole could be improved.

Name _____ Date _____

Mathematical Autobiography

Describe some math experiences that you remember from past school years. Be sure to include your best and worst moments as a mathematics student last year. Also include what expectations you have for yourself this year in math class.

Name _____ Date _____

Portfolio Summary

Write a summary of what you have learned in math class. Be sure to include what you have learned about yourself as a mathematics student and what goals you have for the next grading period.

Teacher's Scavenger Hunt

Complete the scavenger hunt below to learn more about the *Math Thematics* program. Use a student textbook, your *Teacher's Edition*, and this *Teacher's Resource Book* to answer these questions.

1. What are the goals of Module 2 Section 4 Exploration 3? Where can you find the goals stated in the student textbook and in the *Teacher's Edition*?

2. The *Math Thematics* program provides a newsletter that can be shared with parents and others as a description of the mathematics to be learned in each module. What is that feature called? Where can you find it for each module?

3. Each section in the student textbook or *Teacher's Edition* begins with a Setting the Stage, which may be a reading passage, an activity, or a visual display. Find an example of each type of Setting the Stage.

4. Materials Lists are provided in the *Teacher's Edition* for each module and section. Give a few examples of materials needed in Module 2.

5. Where can you find a list of all the Technology Resources available in the *Math Thematics* program?

Find a few sections in the student textbook or *Teacher's Edition* that require the use of a Labsheet.

6. If the Labsheet is needed in a Setting the Stage or an Exploration, how was that indicated on the page?

7. How are you and your students told that a Labsheet will be needed in the Practice and Application Exercises?

8. Where would you find a blackline master for Labsheet 3A, which is needed for Module 2 Section 3?

For Questions 9 and 10, look at Module 1 Section 4 in the student textbook and the *Teacher's Edition*.

9. What is the suggested homework assignment after completing Exploration 1? Where in the section are the homework exercises for Exploration 1 identified for the student?

10. Where in the *Teacher's Edition* is the suggested assignment given for this section?

11. Where can you find additional skill practice, standardized test practice, and study skills support for a section or module?

12. What resources does the *Math Thematics* program provide to help a student who has been absent from class, or to help any student study for a test?

13. Look at the Assessment Scales on either pages 1-6 and 1-7 or pages 2-6 and 2-7 in this *Teacher's Resource Book*. How can these Assessment Scales pages be used by you and your students? (*Hint:* See the information in the *Teacher's Edition*, pages T32–T33, and in this *Teacher's Resource Book*, pages TR-13–TR-21, to help you understand the Assessment Scales.)

14. The student textbook and *Teacher's Edition* include a Review and Assessment for each module. What kind of additional assessments are available to you in the *Teacher's Resource Book* for each module?

15. What pages in the *Teacher's Edition* give a summary of Assessment tools throughout the program?

The student textbook provides an Extended Exploration (E^2) for each module. Questions 16–18 ask you to find materials to accompany these E^2, which appear in other resources.

16. The *Teacher's Edition* gives some background on Managing Extended Explorations. Where is this article located? Where else is information given about the Extended Explorations in this program?

17. Where would you find a possible Solution to the textbook E^2 in Module 2, for example?

18. The program provides an Alternate Extended Exploration (Alternate E^2) for a few modules at each book level. What is the title of the Alternate E^2 for Module 2? Where can it be found?

19. Where is the Scavenger Hunt for your students located? How does it help you and your students understand the student textbook and its resources?

Answers for the Teacher's Scavenger Hunt

1. The goals of Module 2 Section 4 Exploration 3 are "Write equations to solve percent problems." and "Find a representative sample." The goals are listed in the student textbook next to the start of the Exploration. In the *Teacher's Edition*, goals are given on the module planner and section planner pages at the beginning of each module.

2. The *Teacher's Resource Book*s provide a Math Gazette newsletter for each module that can be sent home to families to explain the math to be learned in that module. For example, in this *Teacher's Resource Book for Modules 1 and 2*, Math Gazettes can be found on pages 1-4–1-5 and pages 2-4–2-5. An article in the *Teacher's Edition* on Communicating with Parents, pages T46–T47, may also be helpful.

3. Sample Responses: Examples of Setting the Stage *reading passages* are Module 4 Section 5, Module 6 Section 1, and Module 8 Section 1. Examples of Setting the Stage *activities* are Module 2 Section 1, Module 5 Section 3, and Module 5 Section 5. Examples of Setting the Stage *visual displays* are Module 4 Section 3, Module 4 Section 4, and Module 5 Section 5.

4. Materials Lists are given at point of use in the student textbook and are provided on module planner and section planner pages before each module in the *Teacher's Edition*. Also, a complete Materials List for Book 3 is given on page TR-31 in this *Teacher's Resource Book for Modules 1 and 2*. Examples of materials needed in Module 2 would be colored number cubes, index cards, paper clips, markers, and scissors.

5. A list of technology resources is provided on page T35 in the *Teacher's Edition*.

6. The Set Up in a Setting the Stage or Exploration tells what materials are needed, including a list of any labsheets that are needed. (See, for example, Module 1 Section 1 page 5 in the student textbook or *Teacher's Edition*.)

7. In the Practice and Application Exercises, a side note titled "You Will Need" tells you and your students that a labsheet or other materials are required for listed exercises.

8. A labsheet needed for a section in Module 2 would be found in the *Teacher's Resource Book for Modules 1 and 2*. All resources for a particular section are grouped together so look in Section 3 resources. Labsheet 3A is on page 2-31.

9. The homework exercises identified for Module 1 Section 4 Exploration 1 are Exercises 1–4. These are listed for the student at the end of the Exploration on page 52.

10. In the *Teacher's Edition*, a suggested assignment for this section is given on the Section 4 planner page before the module on page 1J and also at point of use at the beginning of the Practice and Application Exercises on page 57. The assignments in the *Teacher's Edition* indicate which exercises to assign on which days of the Exploration. They also provide suggestions for Core Assignments and Extended Assignments.

11. The *Teacher's Resource Books* provide additional Practice and Applications and Study Guide materials with Exercises for each section in a module, and a Standardized Test covering the topics of the whole module.

12. A student who has been absent from class or who is studying for a test can use the Key Concepts pages in the student textbook. The Study Guide materials available for each section in the *Teacher's Resource Books* would also be helpful.

13. The teacher and student can use the Assessment Scales to actively involve the student in assessing his or her own work. As students become more familiar with the scales, they understand what they need to do to improve their problem solving, reasoning, and communication. Teachers assess students' work using the same scales written from a teacher's point of view. The combination of student and teacher assessment provides important feedback to help students improve.

14. For each module, the *Teacher's Resource Book* includes a Module Diagnostic Test, a Mid-Module Quiz, two Module Tests (Forms A and B), a Module Standardized Test, and a Module Performance Assessment. After every two modules, there is a Cumulative Test covering those two modules. The *Teacher's Resource Books* also include a Pre-Course Test before the Module 1 materials, a Mid-Year Test at the end of the Module 4 materials, and an End-of-Year Test at the end of the Module 8 materials.

15. A summary of Assessment tools is provided on pages T30–T31 in the *Teacher's Edition*.

16. In the *Teacher's Edition*, an article on Managing Extended Explorations is given on pages T44–T45. In this *Teacher's Resource Book for Modules 1 and 2* pages 1-60–1-63, more information is provided on the Format for an Extended Exploration, along with Sample Scoring Profiles and Sample Student Solutions.

17. A sample Solution to the textbook E^2 in Module 2 can be found in this *Teacher's Resource Book for Modules 1 and 2* on page 2-40.

18. An Alternate E^2 for Module 2 can be found in this *Teacher's Resource Book for Modules 1 and 2* on pages 2-41–2-44. It is titled "The Amazing Lake Revisited."

19. The Scavenger Hunt for the students, located on pages xx–xxi in the student textbook (and on pages T56–T57 in the *Teacher's Edition*), helps students identify all the resources in their textbook modules, in the front of the book, and in the back of the book. It is best used at the beginning of the year so that students will know what is available to them (for example, the Table of Contents, Tables, and Glossary) as they progress through the year.

Literature Connections for *Math Thematics* Book 3

Fiction

- *The Mystery of Blacktail Canyon* (Module 3)
- *Black Star, Bright Dawn* by Scott O'Dell (Module 5, page 348)
- "Sidewalk Measles" by Barbara M. Hales from *The Sky is Full of Song* (Module 6, page 392)
- *Charlie and the Chocolate Factory* by Roald Dahl (Module 6, page 420)
- *Two of Everything* by Lily Toy Hong (Module 8, page 518)

Historical Fiction and Nonfiction

- *Seeing Fingers: The Story of Louis Braille* by Etta DeGering (Module 4, page 283)
- *Breakthrough, Tunnelling the Channel* by Derek Wilson (Module 5, page 363)
- *The Perfect Storm* by Sebastian Junger (Module 7, page 465)

Materials List for *Math Thematics* Book 3

This is a complete list of materials needed for Book 3 of *Math Thematics*. All quantities are based on a class of 30 students.

Manipulatives

A classroom set of each is needed.

- Centimeter cubes
- Algebra tiles
- Colored number cubes
- Colored disks

Regular School Supplies

- Graph paper (2250 sheets total, 60 sheets of centimeter graph paper)
- Unlined paper (315 sheets)
- Index cards (3 packages, size: 3 in. × 5 in.)
- Tracing paper (30 sheets)
- Cardstock
- Large sheets of sturdy paper
- Posterboard
- Construction paper (60 sheets)
- Colored pencils or markers (8 boxes)
- Scissors (15–30)
- Transparent tape
- Masking tape
- String (about 100 ft)
- Compasses (30)
- Protractors (30)
- Rulers (15–30, customary and metric)
- Meter sticks (8)
- Yardsticks (8, unless the meter sticks have customary units)
- Tape measure
- Paper clips (30)
- Glue or glue sticks

Technology

- Scientific calculators (30)
- Fraction calculators (30)
- Graphing calculators (30, optional)
- Drawing, spreadsheet, probability, and statistical software (optional)

Additional Supplies

- Modeling clay
- Plastic knife
- Clear plastic cups (8)
- Encyclopedia
- Items for game pieces
- Small object (to be moved)
- Material for building ramps and cylinders
- Package for commercial product
- Drinking straws (31)
- Small balls (30)
- Cans (40, at least five different sizes and shapes)
- Weights or washers (15)
- Clear glass or plastic containers (8, flower vases, juice bottles, and so on)
- Water or rice (for filling containers)

PRE-COURSE TEST

NUMBERS AND OPERATIONS

Decimal Concepts (Toolbox, pp. 579–582)

Replace each ___?___ with >, <, or =.

1. 0.650 __?__ 0.65

2. 0.9 __?__ 0.99

3. 0.2 __?__ 0.02

Find each product.

4. $\begin{array}{r} 251 \\ \times\ 0.9 \\ \hline \end{array}$

5. $\begin{array}{r} 7.65 \\ \times\ 1.2 \\ \hline \end{array}$

6. $\begin{array}{r} 0.088 \\ \times\ 0.06 \\ \hline \end{array}$

Find each quotient. If necessary, round each answer to the nearest hundredth.

7. $10\overline{)560.5}$

8. $16\overline{)780}$

9. $2.7\overline{)26.46}$

Divisibility, Factors, and Multiples (Toolbox, pp. 583–584)

Test each number for divisibility.

10. Is 636 divisible by 4?

11. Is 3852 divisible by 6?

12. Is 52,418 divisible by 8?

Find the GCF and the LCM of each pair of numbers.

13. 18, 45

14. 17, 50

15. 225, 240

Fraction Concepts (Toolbox, pp. 585–588)

Replace each ___?___ with the number that will make the fractions equivalent.

16. $\frac{5}{9} = \frac{?}{18}$

17. $\frac{7}{8} = \frac{?}{40}$

18. $\frac{12}{56} = \frac{?}{14}$

Find each sum, difference, product, or quotient. Write each answer in lowest terms.

19. $\frac{1}{8} + \frac{2}{5}$

20. $\frac{4}{7} - \frac{3}{8}$

21. $\frac{7}{15} + \frac{1}{3}$

22. $\frac{1}{7} \cdot \frac{7}{8}$

23. $\frac{3}{5} \div \frac{6}{25}$

24. $1\frac{1}{8} \cdot \frac{5}{9}$

Write each fraction as a decimal and as a percent.

25. $\frac{3}{25}$

26. $\frac{9}{10}$

27. $\frac{17}{20}$

Order of Operations and Integers (Toolbox, pp. 589–590)

Find each answer.

28. $70 - 20 \cdot 3 + 5$

29. $50 - 4^2 \cdot 2$

30. $2(3 + 2)^2$

Use a number line to write each group of integers in order from least to greatest.

31. 2, 1, –2

32. 0, 6, –5, 3

33. 4, –5, 3, –3

◄◄◄◄◄◄◄◄◄◄◄◄◄◄◄◄◄◄◄ GEOMETRY AND MEASUREMENT

Locating Points in a Coordinate Plane (Toolbox, p. 591)

Use the diagram at the right. Give the coordinates of each point.

34. A

35. B

36. C

37. D

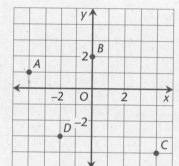

Angles and Triangles (Toolbox, pp. 592–594)

Tell whether each triangle is (a) *acute*, *right*, or *obtuse* and (b) *scalene*, *isosceles*, or *equilateral*.

38.

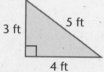

3 ft, 5 ft, 4 ft

39.

96°, 42°, 42°

40.

60°, 60°, 60°

41. Explain why the figure in Exercise 40 is a regular polygon.

Using Formulas from Geometry (Toolbox, p. 595)

Find the volume of each right rectangular prism.

42. base length: 7 m, base width: 3 m, height: 4 m

43. base length: 5 cm, base width: 4 cm, height: 8 cm

◄◄◄◄◄◄◄◄◄◄◄◄◄◄◄◄◄◄◄◄◄◄◄ DATA ANALYSIS

Finding the Mean, Median, Mode, and Range (Toolbox, p. 596)

Find the mean, the median, the mode(s), and the range of each set of data.

44. 20, 18, 7, 18, 20, 13, 16

45. 56, 51, 47, 61, 58, 59, 48, 60

Contents

Book 3	Teacher's Resources for Module 1

Amazing Feats and Facts

Name _____ Date _____

Module Diagnostic Test
For use before Module 1

1. Tell whether the given rates are equivalent or not equivalent. (Sec. 1)

   a. $50/day; $350/week   **b.** 2000 rotations/min; 30 rotations/sec

2. The circle graph shows the percentage of freshmen math classes offered at a high school. (Sec. 1)

   a. What percent of math classes are geometry?

   b. If there are a total of 32 classes offered, how many are basic math or pre-algebra?

   c. Without measuring, give the angle measure of the sector that represents pre-algebra.

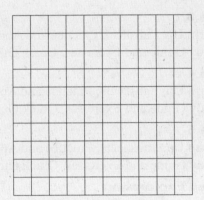

Freshmen Math Classes

3. The average litter sizes of the most prolific wild mammals in the world are given below. Draw a histogram of the litter sizes using intervals of 5. (Sec. 1)

   25, 22, 11, 10, 9, 8.5, 7, 7, 6.5, 6.5

Two classes' percentile scores on a standardized test are shown below. Use the data for Questions 4 and 5. (Sec. 2)

Class Percentile Scores

Class A	61	76	83	50	98	88	88	97	87	76	83	76	73	97	69
Class B	57	96	68	94	58	90	52	68	81	76	85	74			

4. **a.** Use the data to make a back-to-back stem-and-leaf plot.

   b. Find the mean, median, and mode for each class.

Name _____   Date _____

Module Diagnostic Test

For use before Module 1

5. a. Which data set, Class A or Class B, does the box-and-whisker plot at the right represent? Explain how you know.

Class Percentile Scores

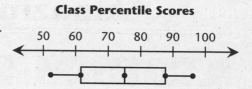

b. Construct a box-and-whisker plot for the other class.

c. Write a brief statement based on the box-and-whisker plots that compares how the classes did on the test.

6. Use inverse operations to solve each equation. Check your solutions.   (Sec. 3)

a. $\dfrac{x}{7} = 14$ **b.** $3y - 7 = 20$ **c.** $45 = 9 + 6m$

7. If possible, combine like terms to simplify each expression.   (Sec. 3)

a. $12x + 8 - 2x$ **b.** $9x^2 + 6x + 8x^2$ **c.** $xy + 2x + y$

8. The data below represents the height of a hot air balloon at a time in minutes.   (Sec. 4)

Time (min)	1	3	5	8	10	11	12
Height (ft)	2200	2440	2700	3050	3420	3520	3600

a. Make a scatter plot of the data comparing height to time. Put time on the horizontal axis.

b. Is there a *positive correlation*, a *negative correlation*, or *no correlation* between the time and the height?

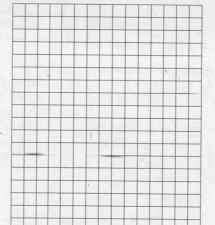

c. Use a straight line or a smooth curve to connect the points.

d. Use your graph to predict the height of the balloon at 15 minutes.

9. The product of two numbers is 36. Their sum is 13. What are the numbers?   (Sec. 5)

10. Find the length of a rectangle with an area of 48 cm^2 and a width of $\dfrac{1}{4}$ cm.   (Sec. 5)

The Math Gazette
Amazing Feats and Facts

Sneak Preview!

Over the next several weeks in our mathematics class, we will be using proportional reasoning and problem solving, working with rates, and learning methods from algebra and statistics while completing a thematic unit on Amazing Feats and Facts. Some of the topics we will be discussing are:

► amazing facts from radio, TV, newspapers, and magazines

► extraordinary rules of thumb

► the winning of the 1986 NBA Slam dunk Competition by a player who was only 5 ft 7 in. tall

► the surprising features of the Lake of the Ozarks

Ask Your Student

What are inverse operations and how could they be used to solve the equation $4x - 3 = 9$? (Sec. 3)

How can you use a person's height to predict the distance he or she can reach with a standing jump? (Sec. 4)

What is so amazing about the Lake of the Ozarks? (Sec. 5)

Connections

Literature:
Students will examine several rules of thumb. They may be interested in reading about other rules of thumb in *Rules of Thumb* or *Rules of Thumb 2*, by Tom Parker.

Popular Media:
Students will use equivalent rates to explore whether claims often seen in newspapers and on television are truly amazing or whether the way the data was reported makes them appear amazing.

Music plays an important part in the lives of most middle school students. In this section, students will explore data about popular and country musicians as they improve their data analysis skills.

Geography:
Students will use tables, graphs, and equations to model relationships between perimeter and area as they investigate Missouri's Lake of the Ozarks.

E² Project

Following Section 5, students will have about one week to complete the Extended Exploration (E²), *A Special Number*. Students will create a 10-digit number in which the first digit tells how many 0s are in the number, the second digit tells how many 1s, and so on.

Module Project

After completing the module, students will use the mathematics they have learned to analyze some of the amazing claims we hear every day. Then students will display their own amazing claims on posters that will be shared with their class.

MISSOURI

Lake of the Ozarks

Amazing Feats and Facts

Section Title	Mathematics Students Will Be Learning	Activities
1: It's Amazing!?	♦ finding and using rates and equivalent rates ♦ creating and interpreting histograms and circle graphs	♦ use rates to determine if facts are realistic ♦ examine data on computer usage and access to the Internet
2: Amazing Musicians	♦ making and analyzing back-to-back stem-and-leaf plots ♦ creating and interpreting box-and-whisker plots ♦ choosing an appropriate data display	♦ investigate the ages and accomplishments of famous musicians
3: Extraordinary Rules of Thumb	♦ writing and solving equations ♦ identifying like and unlike terms ♦ simplifying expressions ♦ applying the distributive properties of multiplication over addition and subtraction	♦ work with rules of thumb ♦ use inverse operations to solve equations
4: Athletic Triumphs	♦ making and interpreting scatter plots ♦ fitting a line to data points on a scatter plot and using it to make predictions	♦ collect and analyze data about height and jumping distance ♦ graph data ♦ analyze data about the Tour de France
5: An Amazing Lake	♦ using a 4-step approach to problem solving ♦ using tables, graphs, and equations to model relationships	♦ analyze amazing facts about the Lake of the Ozarks ♦ draw rectangles with a fixed area but different perimeters

Activities to do at Home

♦ Search for "amazing facts" on the Internet and visit some of the sites to learn more amusing and incredible facts. (After Sec. 1)

♦ Look up information on the career of one of your student's favorite recording artists. Compare the data to that of the musicians discussed in Section 2. (After Sec. 2)

♦ Collect jumping data for family members of different ages to see whether the pattern found for classmates holds. (After Sec. 4)

Related Topics

You may want to discuss these related topics with your student:

 Top ten recordings

 Bicycle racing

 Tourist attractions

 Rules of thumb

Name _____   Problem _____

 Teacher Assessment Scales
For use with Module 1

☆ *The star indicates that you excelled in some way.*

 Problem Solving

❶ ❷ ❸ ❹ ❺ ☆→

❶ You did not understand the problem well enough to get started or you did not show any work.

❸ You understood the problem well enough to make a plan and to work toward a solution.

❺ You made a plan, you used it to solve the problem, and you verified your solution.

 Mathematical Language

❶ ❷ ❸ ❹ ❺ ☆→

❶ You did not use any mathematical vocabulary or symbols, or you did not use them correctly, or your use was not appropriate.

❸ You used appropriate mathematical language, but the way it was used was not always correct or other terms and symbols were needed.

❺ You used mathematical language that was correct and appropriate to make your meaning clear.

 Representations

❶ ❷ ❸ ❹ ❺ ☆→

❶ You did not use any representations such as equations, tables, graphs, or diagrams to help solve the problem or explain your solution.

❸ You made appropriate representations to help solve the problem or help you explain your solution, but they were not always correct or other representations were needed.

❺ You used appropriate and correct representations to solve the problem or explain your solution.

 Connections

❶ ❷ ❸ ❹ ❺ ☆→

❶ You attempted or solved the problem and then stopped.

❸ You found patterns and used them to extend the solution to other cases, or you recognized that this problem relates to other problems, mathematical ideas, or applications.

❺ You extended the ideas in the solution to the general case, or you showed how this problem relates to other problems, mathematical ideas, or applications.

 Presentation

❶ ❷ ❸ ❹ ❺ ☆→

❶ The presentation of your solution and reasoning is unclear to others.

❸ The presentation of your solution and reasoning is clear in most places, but others may have trouble understanding parts of it.

❺ The presentation of your solution and reasoning is clear and can be understood by others.

Content Used: _____   **Computational Errors:**   Yes ☐   No ☐

Notes on Errors: _____

_____

Math Thematics, Book 3
Teacher's Resource Book, Modules 1 and 2

Name _____   Problem _____

Student Self-Assessment Scales

For use with Module 1

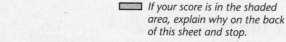 If your score is in the shaded area, explain why on the back of this sheet and stop.

☆ The star indicates that you excelled in some way.

 ## Problem Solving

❶ ❷ ❸ ❹ ❺ ☆

❶ I did not understand the problem well enough to get started or I did not show any work.

❸ I understood the problem well enough to make a plan and to work toward a solution.

❺ I made a plan, I used it to solve the problem, and I verified my solution.

 ## Mathematical Language

❶ ❷ ❸ ❹ ❺ ☆

❶ I did not use any mathematical vocabulary or symbols, or I did not use them correctly, or my use was not appropriate.

❸ I used appropriate mathematical language, but the way it was used was not always correct or other terms and symbols were needed.

❺ I used mathematical language that was correct and appropriate to make my meaning clear.

 ## Representations

❶ ❷ ❸ ❹ ❺ ☆

❶ I did not use any representations such as equations, tables, graphs, or diagrams to help solve the problem or explain my solution.

❸ I made appropriate representations to help solve the problem or help me explain my solution, but they were not always correct or other representations were needed.

❺ I used appropriate and correct representations to solve the problem or explain my solution.

 ## Connections

❶ ❷ ❸ ❹ ❺ ☆

❶ I attempted or solved the problem and then stopped.

❸ I found patterns and used them to extend the solution to other cases, or I recognized that this problem relates to other problems, mathematical ideas, or applications.

❺ I extended the ideas in the solution to the general case, or I showed how this problem relates to other problems, mathematical ideas, or applications.

 ## Presentation

❶ ❷ ❸ ❹ ❺ ☆

❶ The presentation of my solution and reasoning is unclear to others.

❸ The presentation of my solution and reasoning is clear in most places, but others may have trouble understanding parts of it.

❺ The presentation of my solution and reasoning is clear and can be understood by others.

Warm-Up Exercises
For use with Section 1

Complete each of the following to find the equivalent measure.

1. 360 sec = _____ min

2. 3 pt = _____ c

3. 4 yd = _____ in.

4. 2 yd^2 = _____ ft^2

5. 8 oz = _____ lb

6. 4400 yd = _____ mi

ANSWERS

1. 6 min   2. 6 c   3. 144 in.   4. 18 ft^2 5. $\frac{1}{2}$ lb   6. 2.5 mi

Math Thematics, Book 3
Teacher's Resource Book, Modules 1 and 2

Name _____ Date _____

Circle Graph (Use with Question 12 on page 5.)

Directions

1. Find the percent of adult Internet users in each age group. Round your answers to the nearest percent and record them in the table.

2. For each age group, use a protractor to measure the angle of the corresponding sector of the circle graph. Record the angle measures in the table.

3. Find the percent of the whole circle (360°) taken up by each sector. Round your answers to the nearest percent and record them in the table.

4. What do you notice about the percents in steps 1 and 3?

Adults Who Used the Internet at Home in 2003				
Age group	**Number**	**Percent of all adults who used the Internet at home**	**Angle measure of sector**	**Percent of total measure (360°)**
18 to 24	16,438,000			
25 to 34	23,951,000			
35 to 44	29,391,000			
45 to 54	27,563,000			
55 and over	28,413,000			
Total	125,756,000			

**Adults Who Used the
Internet at Home in 2003**

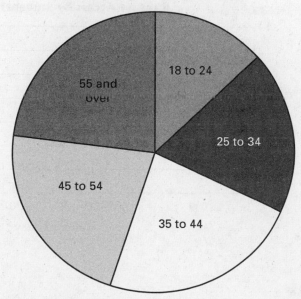

MODULE 1   **LABSHEET** **1B**

Histograms (Use with Questions 19–23 on page 8.)

Directions

a. In the first table, make a tally of the numbers of Internet accesses per day that lie within each interval, and record the corresponding frequency. The first two rows have been completed for you.

b. Use the table to draw a histogram on the first set of axes.

c. Complete the second table and use it to draw a histogram on the second set of axes.

Internet Access by Students at School

16, 27, 26, 5, 11, 33, 23, 17, 15, 20, 3, 14, 29, 21, 23,

31, 16, 8, 14, 28, 19, 20, 24, 35, 7, 12, 22, 27, 18, 20

Internet Access by Students at School		
Times per day	Tally	Frequency
0–4	I	1
5–9	III	3
10–14		
15–19		
20–24		
25–29		
30–34		
35–39		

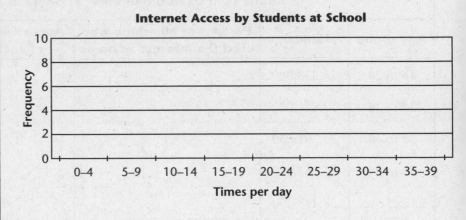

Internet Access by Students at School		
Times per day	Tally	Frequency
0–9		
10–19		
20–29		
30–39		

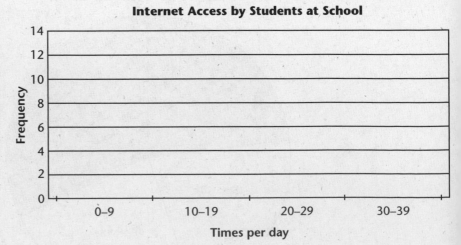

Math Thematics, Book 3
Teacher's Resource Book, Modules 1 and 2

Name _____   Date _____

Practice and Applications
For use with Section 1

For use with Exploration 1

1. Name the units in each rate. Then write a unit rate.

   a. 442 mi in 8.5 hr

   b. 3 lb for $8.43

   c. 82 mi for 4.5 gal

   d. 87 chirps in 3 min

2. Complete each equation.

   a. 1.5 mi/min = __?__ mi/hr

   b. $1.92 per lb = __?__ per oz

   c. $18,500 salary per year = __?__ per week

   d. 42 hr/week = __?__ hr/day

3. It takes the space shuttle about 8 minutes to climb 70 miles. What is the shuttle's rate of ascent?

4. The Humphrey family traveled 320 miles in 7.5 hours.

   a. What was their average rate of speed?

   b. At the same average rate of speed, how far can they travel in 9 hours?

   c. Change the rate to miles per minute.

   d. How long does it take to travel exactly one mile?

5. Write a word problem for each calculation. Solve the problem.

   a. 70 mi/hr • 3.5 hr

   b. 21 mi/gal • 6.2 gal

   c. $2.50 per lb • 4 lb

   d. $5.25 per hour • 4 hr

6. One of the longest nonstop airplane flights is between Johannesburg, South Africa, and New York.

   a. If the 7983 mile flight takes 15 hours 5 minutes, what is the average rate of speed per hour?

   b. What is average rate of speed per minute?

   c. At the same rate of speed, how far could the airplane travel in 20 hours?

(continued)

Name _____   Date _____

Practice and Applications
For use with Section 1

For use with Exploration 2

Technology **Use the circle graph shown for Exercises 7–9.**

7. What percentage of European households were on-line in 1996?

8. Without measuring, give the angle measure that corresponds to each section of the circle graph.

9. If there were 100,000,000 households in the U.S. in 1996, how many of them would you expect to be on-line?

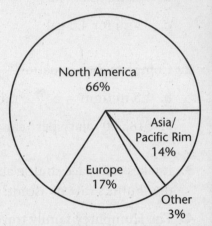

World On-line Households, 1996

10. The chart at the right shows how the population of the world was distributed in 1996. Draw a circle graph of the data.

Country	Percent
China	21.3
India	16.5
U.S.	4.6
Indonesia	3.6
Other	54.0

11. Social Studies The age structure of a country is used as an indicator of the health of the population of the country. The age structure of selected countries is shown in the table below. For each country in the table, draw a circle graph that shows the age structure of the country.

Country	0–14 years	15–64 years	65 years & older
Afghanistan	43%	54%	3%
Denmark	17%	67%	16%
U.S.	22%	65%	13%
Russia	21%	67%	12%

12. Writing Charlene said that the data she collected would not make a good circle graph. Her data were the birth year and height of students in her class. Was she right? How do you know? How could she restructure the data so that a circle graph would be appropriate?

(continued)

Math Thematics, Book 3
Teacher's Resource Book, Modules 1 and 2

Practice and Applications

For use with Section 1

13. The data table at the right represents the test grades for an eighth grade class.

48	52	55	56
57	58	59	60
62	65	68	69
70	71	71	78
80	85	87	89
91	91	92	95
98	98	99	99

   a. Draw a histogram of the data set using intervals of 10 points.

   b. Draw a histogram of the data set using intervals of 25 points.

Health **The percent of the population with high serum cholesterol (a level greater than or equal to 240 mg/dL) in 1994 is shown for both men and women at the right.**

	Men	Women
25–34 years	8.2	7.3
35–44 years	19.4	12.3
45–54 years	26.6	26.7
55–64 years	28	40.9
65–74 years	21.9	41.3

For Exercises 14 and 15, draw a histogram of the given data set. Use the same intervals for both histograms. Note: the over 75 years category is omitted.

14. percent of men with high cholesterol   **15.** percent of women with high cholesterol

16. **Interpreting Data** Use the histograms from Exercises 14 and 15 to draw a conclusion about how the percent of men with high cholesterol compares with the percent of women with high cholesterol.

17. The age category "75 and older" was omitted from the table. Explain why you cannot use this interval to make a histogram.

18. For Exercises 14 and 15, the mean serum cholesterol in mg/dL could have been given instead of the percent. For example, in the 35–44 age category for men, the mean serum cholesterol is 206 mg/dL, while the female mean serum cholesterol is 195 mg/dL. Would these have been better statistics to convey information about high cholesterol levels? Why or why not?

Name _____   Date _____

Study Guide
For use with Section 1

It's Amazing!?   Rates and Data Displays

GOAL   **LEARN HOW TO:** • use rates
                                • find equivalent rates
                                • draw and interpret circle graphs
                                • draw and interpret histograms

     AS YOU: • determine if facts are realistic
                  • examine facts

Exploration 1: Using Rates

Rates

A **rate** is a ratio that compares two quantities measured in different units.
Rates describe how one quantity depends on another. For example, if you
went on a hike and it took you 3 hours to hike 9 miles, the rate would be
expressed as "9 miles in 3 hours."

Equivalent rates are equal rates that may be expressed using different
units. For example, 60 mi/hr and 1 mi/min are equivalent rates.

A rate is often easier to understand if it is expressed as a *unit rate*. A **unit
rate** is a ratio that compares a quantity to one unit of another quantity.

Example

Change the rate to a unit rate:

You pay $6.50 for 5 pairs of socks.

Sample Response

$$\frac{\$6.50}{5 \text{ pairs of socks}} = \frac{\$6.50 \div 5}{5 \text{ pairs of socks} \div 5}$$

$$= \frac{\$1.30}{1 \text{ pair of socks}} \quad \text{or } \$1.30 \text{ per pair of socks}$$

Name _____   Date _____

Study Guide
For use with Section 1

Exploration 2: Circle Graphs and Histograms

Making Circle Graphs

A **frequency table** shows the **frequency,** or number, of items in each category or numerical interval.

Data from a frequency table can be used to make a circle graph. A **circle graph** shows the division of a whole into parts, each represented by a slice of the whole circle, called a **sector**.

Example

A rug company asked 40 customers in which room the carpet is cleaned most often. Of these, 20 said the family room, 10 said the dining room, 6 said the kitchen, and 4 said their child's bedroom. Use a circle graph to display these results.

▬ Sample Response ▬

Step 1: Organize the data in a table.

Response	Number	Percent	Angle measure
family room	20	$\frac{20}{40} = 50\%$	$0.5 \times 360° = 180°$
dining room	10	$\frac{10}{40} = 25\%$	$0.25 \times 360° = 90°$
kitchen	6	$\frac{6}{40} = 15\%$	$0.15 \times 360° = 54°$
child's bedroom	4	$\frac{4}{40} = 10\%$	$0.10 \times 360° = 36°$

To find each angle measure, multiply the percent expressed as a decimal by 360°.

Step 2: Use a compass to draw a circle. Use a protractor to draw sectors having the angle measures found in the table.

Give the graph a title.

Label each sector with the corresponding response and percent.

Carpet Cleaned Most Often

The sum of the percents in a circle graph must be 100%.

The sum of the angle measures in a circle must be 360°.

Name _____   Date _____

Study Guide
For use with Section 1

Histograms

A **histogram** shows the frequencies of numerical values that fall within intervals of equal width.

Example

Draw a histogram to display the temperature data given in the frequency table.

Temp. (°F)	Frequency
41–50	8
51–60	18
61–70	4

■ Sample Response ■

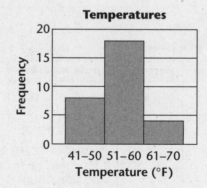

The height of each bar is the frequency of temperatures in the corresponding interval.

The intervals in the graph are the same as the intervals in the table.

Name _____   Date _____

MODULE 1 Study Guide: Practice & Application Exercises

For use with Section 1

Exploration 1

Name the units in each rate. Then write a unit rate.

1. 186 pages from 31 students

2. 18.75 miles in 25 min

3. $15.81 for 3 boxes

4. 192 mi per 6 gal of gas

Complete each equation.

5. $0.50/day = ___?___ per week

6. 3600 lb/hr = ___?___ lb/min

7. $5.52/ft = ___?___ per in.

8. 3 vials/oz = ___?___ vials/c

Exploration 2

Use the circle graph at the right.

9. What percent of families surveyed own 3 or more TVs?

10. Without measuring, give the angle measure of the sector for families owning 2 TVs.

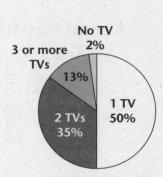

11. Draw a circle graph that shows the percent of truck sales at Auto World for the years listed in the table. Round each percent to the nearest whole percent.

2003	2004	2005	2006	2007
34	27	27	36	46

The cost of groceries for the Morales family for each month of 2007 are given below.

$420 $509 $225 $235 $350 $400 $450 $250 $315 $480 $505 $335

12. Draw a histogram of the data using intervals of $100.

13. Draw a histogram of the data using intervals of $50.

14. Can you make a histogram of the cost of groceries for each week? Explain.

Name _____ Date _____

Quick Quiz

For use after Section 1

1. Tell whether the given rates are equivalent.

   a. 32 ft/sec; 1920 ft/min   **b.** 8.4 gal/day; 2 qt/hr

2. The world record for the 100-meter butterfly swim set in 1999 was 51.81 sec. What was the average rate per second?

3. Describe how to determine the percentage of each ingredient.

Cereal Nutrition

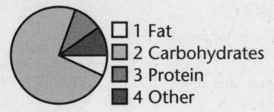

☐ 1 Fat
☐ 2 Carbohydrates
☐ 3 Protein
■ 4 Other

4. Draw a histogram of the test score data using intervals of 10:

64, 66, 66, 71, 72, 75, 75, 78, 79, 82, 85, 85, 87, 90, 91, 94

Warm-Up Exercises
For use with Section 2

**Order each set of numbers from least to greatest.
Then find the median.**

1. 2.02, 3.2, 0.2, 0.02, 22.0, 2.22

2. 33, 333, 303, 3300, 3, 30, 3003

ANSWERS

1. 0.02, 0.2, 2.02, 2.22, 3.2, 22.0; median: 2.12
2. 3, 30, 33, 303, 333, 3003, 3300; median: 303

MODULE 1   LABSHEET **2A**

Top 40 Hits Stem-and-Leaf Plot (Use with Questions 11–13 on pages 19–20.)

**Number of Top 40 Singles Each Artist
Had from 1990–1999**

```
0 | 7 8 9 9 9 9 9 9 9
1 | 0 0 0 0 0 1 2 2 2 4 4 6 6
2 | 0 0 1 6
```

2 | 0 means 20 Top 40 singles.

Top 40 Hits Box-and-Whisker Plots (Use with Questions 12–14 on pages 19–20)

Directions

• Find the lower extreme, lower quartile, median, upper quartile, and upper extreme of the number of Top 40 hits. Record these values in the table.

• Draw a box-and-whisker plot for the 1990s artists directly below the box-and-whisker plot for the 1960s artists.

Lower Extreme	
Lower Quartile	
Median	
Upper Quartile	
Upper Extreme	

Number of Top 40 Hits Each Artist Had During the 1960s or 1990s

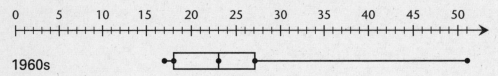

```
    0    5   10   15   20   25   30   35   40   45   50
```

1960s

1990s

Math Thematics, Book 3

Name _____   Date _____

Ages of Winners of the Academy Award for Best Original Song (1960s and 1990s)

Box-and-Whisker Plots (Use with Question 15 on page 20.)

Directions

- Use the data in the table to find the lower extreme, lower quartile, median, upper quartile, and upper extreme for the ages of winners of the Academy Award for best original song for each decade listed.

- Decide on a scale that is best for drawing both box-and-whisker plots on the same number line.

- Draw two box-and-whisker plots that show how the ages of the 1960s winners compare to those of the 1990s winners.

Ages of Winners of the Academy Award for Best Original Song

Year	Composer/Lyricist	Age	Year	Composer/Lyricist	Age
1960	Manos Hadjidakis	35	1965	Paul Francis Webster	33
1961	Henry Mancini	38	1966	John Barry	29
1961	Johnny Mercer	52	1966	Don Black	37
1962	Henry Mancini	39	1967	Leslie Bricusse	27
1962	Johnny Mercer	53	1968	Michel Legrand	44
1963	James Van Heusen	51	1968	Alan Bergman	39
1963	Sammy Cahn	51	1968	Marilyn Bergman	42
1964	Richard M. Sherman	37	1969	Burt Bacharach	49
1964	Robert B. Sherman	39	1969	Hal David	33
1965	Johnny Mandel	40			

Year	Composer/Lyricist	Age	Year	Composer/Lyricist	Age
1990	Stephen Sondheim	61	1995	Alan Menken	47
1991	Alan Menken	43	1995	Stephen Schwartz	49
1991	Howard Ashman	42	1996	Andrew Lloyd Webber	49
1992	Alan Menken	44	1996	Tim Rice	52
1992	Tim Rice	48	1997	James Horner	45
1993	Bruce Springsteen	45	1997	Will Jenning	54
1994	Elton John	48	1998	Stephen Schwartz	52
1994	Tim Rice	50	1999	Phil Collins	49

Name _____   Date _____

Practice and Applications
For use with Section 2

For use with Exploration 1

The heights of an 8th grade class are given below. Use the data for Exercises 1–2.

Heights of Eighth Grade Class, in Inches

60	62	64	63	70	66	68	67	67	59	71	58	67	72	71	59	73
56	58	55	59	61	62	60	61	59	64	65	58	62	61	68	60	60

1. Make a stem-and-leaf plot of the data set.

2. **a.** Find the range of the data in the stem-and-leaf plot.

   b. Find the mean, median, and mode of the data.

   c. Which average do you think best represents the data? Explain.

The table below shows points scored for the first 13 games of the Chicago Bulls and the Utah Jazz during the 1996–1997 National Basketball Association playoff series. Use the same data set for Exercises 3–5. (Note: these games were not played against each other.)

NBA Playoff Scores

Chicago	98	109	96	100	95	100	89	107	84	75	98	80	100
Utah	106	105	104	93	103	84	110	98	101	104	100	92	96

3. **a.** Use the data to make a back-to-back stem-and-leaf plot that compares the scores for each team.

   b. Compare the shapes of the two stem-and-leaf plots. What do the shapes tell you about the scores of each team?

   c. Compare the ranges of the two data sets. What do the ranges tell you about the number of points each team scores per game?

4. **a.** Find the mean, median, and mode of the data for each team.

   b. Which average from part (a) do you think best represents the data? Explain.

5. Chicago went on to defeat Utah in the championship series. Explain why you could not use the previous playoff scores to predict this.

(continued)

Name _____   Date _____

Practice and Applications
For use with Section 2

For use with Exploration 2

The box-and-whisker plot below represents the heights of 8th graders from Exploration 1.

Heights of Eighth Grade Class (in inches)

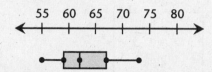

6. a. About what percent of the heights are included in the box portion of the box-and-whisker plot?

b. What do the sizes of the box portions tell you about the heights of the eighth grade students?

c. About what percent of students were between 62 inches and 73 inches tall?

d. How are the least and greatest values from the stem-and-leaf plot from Exploration 1 shown in the box-and-whisker plot?

Use the data for the NBA playoff scores from Exploration 1 and the box-and-whisker plots below for Exercises 7–9.

7. For each box-and-whisker plot, find the values below.

a. the lower extreme

b. the upper extreme

c. the lower quartile

d. the upper quartile

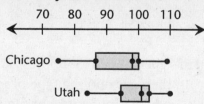

8. a. About what percent of Chicago's scores were below 100?

b. About what percent of Utah's scores were above 101?

9. a. Writing Explain how to use the box-and-whisker plot to compare the median score for each team.

b. Which team had at least 50% of its scores greater than its mean?

(continued)

Name _____   Date _____

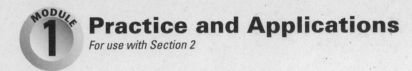

Practice and Applications
For use with Section 2

For use with Exploration 3

Science **The tables below give the weight and length of the nine smallest bats in the world.**

Weight (g)	Length (cm)
2.0	2.9
2.5	3.8
3.0	3.8
3.0	3.8
3.5	4.0

Weight (g)	Length (cm)
3.5	4.0
4.0	3.6
5.0	3.7
5.0	4.3

For Exercises 10–13, make a data display that shows the information specified. Tell why you chose that type of display.

10. the number of bats that weigh between 2.0 and 2.9 grams

11. the number of bats listed that have a length of 3.8 cm

12. the relationship between the weight and length of the bats

13. the median length of the bats listed

14. Open-ended Describe a data set that can be shown using the given type of display.

    a. histogram   **b.** stem-and-leaf plot

    c. circle graph   **d.** scatter plot

15. Open-ended Suppose you conduct a survey asking the participants their age and the type of music they like most. Also note if the participant is male or female.

    a. Suppose you want to display the survey results in a histogram. What are four age categories you could use?

    b. Suppose you want to display the survey results in a circle graph. What are some categories you could use?

    c. Suppose you want to display the survey results in a bar graph. What are sample responses you could use as categories?

Name _____ Date _____

Study Guide
For use with Section 2

Amazing Musicians Displaying Data

GOAL **LEARN HOW TO:** • make and use stem-and-leaf plots
• use box-and-whisker plots to analyze and compare data
• choose the best display for a given situation

AS YOU: • analyze and investigate facts about famous musicians

Exploration 1: Stem-and-Leaf Plots

A **stem-and-leaf plot** displays data in an organized format. The data items are usually ordered from least to greatest.

Usually the digit in the ones place forms the **leaf** for each data value. The leaves are ordered horizontally from least to greatest.

Then the remaining digit or digits of each data value form the **stem** for the corresponding leaf. The stems are ordered vertically, usually from least to greatest.

Example

The following list of numbers represents the number of years the top 15 players in the National Hockey League have played on major teams of the NHL at the start of the 1992–93 season.

13, 26, 18, 18, 22, 17, 23, 17, 17, 24, 21, 20, 20, 15, 12

Use a stem-and-leaf plot to find the mean, the median, and the mode of this data.

Sample Response

In the stem-and-leaf plot below, each **stem** represents a tens digit and each **leaf** represents the corresponding ones digit.

Years Played in NHL by Top 15 Players

```
1 | 2 3 5 7 7 7 8 8          ← The leaves are written in order from
2 | 0 0 1 2 3 4 6              least to greatest.
```

1 | 2 represents the data value 12.

The median is the number represented by the 8th leaf (of 15) counting from left to right beginning in the top row. This leaf represents the data value 18.

The mode is identified by the leaf (or leaves) that occurs in one row more often than all the other leaves in the plot. Here, the leaf 7 occurs three times in the first row. This leaf represents the data value 17.

The mean of the data is $18\frac{13}{15}$.

Study Guide
For use with Section 2

Exploration 2: Box-and-Whisker Plots

A **box-and-whisker plot** shows how data are distributed by dividing the data items into 4 groups. The five values that separate these groups are the *lower extreme, lower quartile, median, upper quartile,* and *upper extreme.* Each group contains about the same number of data items, or about 25% of all the data items. The **lower extreme** and **upper extreme** are the least and greatest data values, respectively. While the median is the middle item (or mean of the two middle items) of all the data values, the **lower quartile** is the median of the data values that occur before the median in an ordered list. Similarly, the **upper quartile** is the median of the data values that occur after the median in an ordered list.

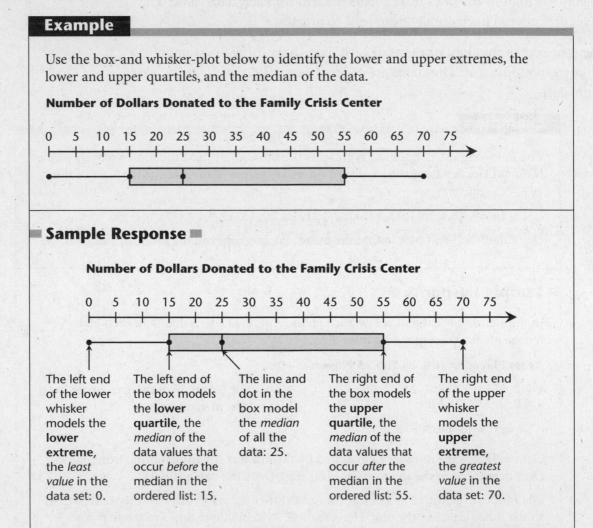

Name _____ Date _____

Study Guide
For use with Section 2

Exploration 3: Choosing a Data Display

Choosing an Appropriate Data Display

You can use bar graphs, histograms, box-and-whisker plots, stem-and-leaf plots, scatter plots, line graphs, and circle graphs to display data. When deciding what type of display to use, consider the type and number of data sets you have, as well as the aspect of the data you want to emphasize.

Example

Which display best shows the median inches of snowfall in January?

Which display best shows that 0–5 inches of snow fell on about 75% of the days in January?

From which display could you most easily tell that there was no snowfall in the interval of 11–15 inches in January?

Inches of Snowfall in January   **Inches of Snowfall in January**

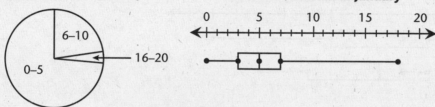

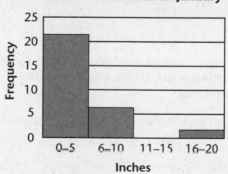

Sample Response

The box-and-whisker plot is the only data display that shows the median inches of snowfall in January. The circle graph best shows that 0–5 inches of snow fell on about 75% of the days in January. The histogram most readily shows that there was no snowfall in the interval of 11–15 inches in January.

Math Thematics, Book 3

Name _____ Date _____

Study Guide: Practice & Application Exercises

For use with Section 2

Exploration 1

Use the data in the table for Exercises 1 and 2.

1. Make a back-to-back stem-and-leaf plot that compares the Test A scores and the Test B scores. What do the shapes of the stem-and-leaf plots tell you about the distribution of the scores on two tests?

2. Find the mean, the median, and the mode for each set of scores.

Scores on Tests A and B			
Test A		Test B	
88	86	55	75
96	75	88	99
100	76	66	98
68	72	78	75
50	75	85	65

Exploration 2

For each box-and-whisker plot, find the values below.

Age of Patients Having Appendicitis in April

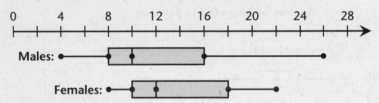

3. the lower extreme

4. the upper extreme

5. the lower quartile

6. the upper quartile

Exploration 3

Tell which type of data display best does each of the following. Explain your thinking.

7. shows the relationship between the number of patents applied for and the number obtained in the past four years

8. compares the acreage of park systems in Texas, Florida, Washington, and California

9. shows that a company's sales have decreased each month since June

10. shows the median, the quartiles, the extremes, and the range of lawyer salaries in New York

11. displays individual race times for 50 runners in a marathon

12. shows the relationship between plant height and hours of sun exposure

Name _____   Date _____

Quick Quiz
For use after Section 2

The table shows percentile scores on a standardized test for two classes.

Class Percentile Scores

Class A	79	84	93	98	85	84	78	62	54	59	68	78	85	84	79
Class B	96	90	77	69	72	79	92	86	85	48	89	77	75	90	90

1. a. Use the data to make a back-to-back stem-and-leaf plot that compares the classes by percentile scores.

b. Find the mean, the median, and the mode for each data set.

2. a. Which data set, Class A or Class B, does the box-and-whisker plot at the right represent? Explain how you know.

Class Percentile Scores

50 60 70 80 90 100

b. Construct a box-and-whisker plot for the other class.

c. Write a brief statement based on the box-and-whisker plots that compares how the classes did on the test.

3. The data below gives the number of times since 1970 that each artist has won Country Music Academy's Entertainer of the Year.

2, 3, 1, 1, 6, 1, 3, 5, 1, 1, 1, 1, 1, 1, 1, 1, 1, 2, 1, 1

a. Why would a stem-and-leaf plot not be a helpful display for this data?

b. What other type of data display would be appropriate? Explain.

Name _____   Date _____

Mid-Module Quiz
For use after Section 2

1. Name the units in each rate. Then write a unit rate.

   a. 440 mi in 8 hr   b. $8.25 for 3 lb of meat

Two cable television companies offer many service packages. The monthly dollar costs of the different packages are shown in the table. Use the table for Questions 2–4.

National Cable	32	44	37	54	64	39	46	39	58
American Cable	28	32	46	51	37	35	54	48	46

2. a. Use the data to make a back-to-back stem-and-leaf plot for the data in the table.

   b. What does the plot tell you about the cost of service offered by each company?

   c. Find the mean, median, mode, and range for each data set.

3. The box-and-whisker plot displays the data for National Cable from the table. Find the

   a. lower extreme.

   b. upper extreme.

   c. lower quartile.

   d. upper quartile.

Cost of Cable Service

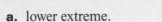

National Cable

American Cable

4. Draw a box-and-whisker plot for American Cable directly below the one for National Cable.

The circle graph shows the percentage of language classes offered at a high school.

5. What percentage of language classes are French?

6. If there are a total of 20 classes offered, how many are German or Russian?

7. Without measuring, give the angle measure of the sector that represents Spanish.

World Language Classes

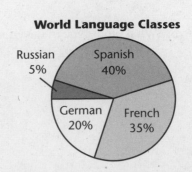

Name _____   Date _____

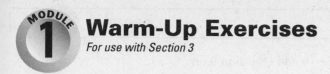

Warm-Up Exercises
For use with Section 3

Solve each equation using mental math.

1. $x + 7 = 12$

2. $23 - m = 20$

3. $4 \cdot p = 36$

4. $\dfrac{s}{3} = 1$

Simplify each expression.

5. $(4 + 3)^2 - 8 \cdot 2$

6. $1 + (16 - 4 \cdot 3)^2 - 9$

ANSWERS

1. 5   2. 3   3. 9   4. 3   5. 33   6. 8

MODULE 1   LABSHEET **3A**

Writing Equations (Use with Question 6 on page 34 and Question 9 on page 35.)

Directions

• Rewrite each rule of thumb as an equation in words.

• Underline any phrases that will be represented by variables.

• Circle words that indicate an equal sign and any operation such as +, −, ×, or ÷.

• Write the equation using numbers, variables, and operational symbols.

Example: You can tell how many miles you are from a thunderstorm by counting the seconds between the lightning and the thunder and dividing by five.

The number of miles from a thunderstorm (is equal to) the seconds between
lightning and thunder (divided) by 5.

$$m \qquad = \qquad s \;\div\; 5$$

1. A college student should plan to spend 3 hours per week studying outside of class for each hour spent in class.

2. You should plan to add about 1.5 pounds of gravel to a home aquarium for each gallon of water in the aquarium.

3. To estimate the temperature outdoors in degrees Fahrenheit, count the number of times one snowy tree cricket chirps in fifteen seconds and add thirty-nine.

4. For dogs 2 years and older, you can find the equivalent human age by multiplying the dog's age by 4 and adding 15.

5. To estimate the temperature in degrees Fahrenheit given the temperature in degrees Celsius, double the temperature in degrees Celsius and add 30.

6. A pilot can estimate how far in nautical miles from the landing point to begin descending by dividing the plane's altitude in feet by 300.

Name _____ Date _____

 MODULE 1

Practice and Applications
For use with Section 3

For use with Exploration 1

1. The depth of the roots of a tree is about one third the height of the tree. Which equation represents this rule of thumb? Let r = the depth of the roots and t = the height of the tree.

   A. $t = \frac{1}{3}r$ **B.** $r = \frac{1}{3}t$ **C.** $r = 3t$

For Exercises 2–5, use variables to write each word sentence as an equation. Tell what each variable represents.

2. The total cost of tickets for the 8th grade to attend a concert is $6 per student times the number of students.

3. To estimate the amount of interest on a savings account for one year, multiply the interest rate of 0.05 by the amount of savings.

4. The total distance of a car trip divided by 50 gives the approximate number of hours the trip will take.

5. To estimate the circumference of a circle, multiply the diameter by 3.

For use with Exploration 2

Check whether $x = 9$ is a solution for each equation below.

6. $3x - 1 = 28$ 7. $x - 9 = 0$ 8. $5 = \frac{x}{3} + 2$

9. $8x + 11 = 85$ 10. $41 = 7x - 22$ 11. $2x + 6 = 21$

**Use inverse operations to solve each equation.
Check your solution.**

12. $5 + x = 27$ 13. $7t = 28$ 14. $2y - 4 = 20$

15. $x - 8 = 4$ 16. $17 = 3t$ 17. $18 = m - 4$

18. $5 + 2d = 22$ 19. $\frac{r}{3} = 18$ 20. $\frac{p}{4} - 1 = 19$

21. To estimate your safe heart rate during exercise, subtract your age from 220 and then multiply by 0.55. Write an equation and find your safe heart rate if you are 35 years old.

(continued)

Name _____ Date _____

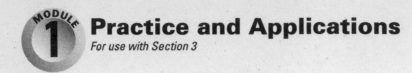

Practice and Applications
For use with Section 3

For use with Exploration 3

22. Which of the terms below are like terms?

$$x^2 \quad \frac{3}{4}x \quad xy \quad xy^2 \quad x^2y \quad 5x^2$$

If possible, combine like terms to simplify each expression.

23. $5x + 12 - 4$ **24.** $6t - 7st$ **25.** $2y + 4x - 2y$

26. $12x^2 - 8x + 6y^2$ **27.** $8t + 16 - 3t$ **28.** $2x^2 + 8x + 5x^2$

29. $5xy^2 + 6xy^2$ **30.** $12x + 8x + 6$ **31.** $3x^2 + 12 - 3x^2$

32. The perimeter of a square is given by the formula $P = 4l$, where l = the length. Find the perimeter of a square with l = 12 cm.

33. Find the perimeter of each rectangle below.

a.
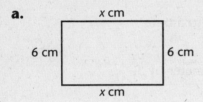

b.
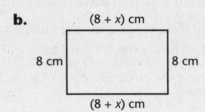

34. The perimeter of a rectangle is represented by the formula $P = 2l + 2w$.

  a. If l = 8 cm and w = 7 cm, what is the perimeter?

  b. Solve for w when P = 80 cm and l = 16 cm.

  c. Find the length and width of a square with perimeter 81 cm.

Name _____   Date _____

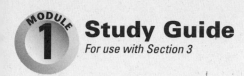

Study Guide
For use with Section 3

Extraordinary Rules of Thumb   Equations and Expressions

GOAL   **LEARN HOW TO:** • write equations from words
                           • solve equations
                           • simplify expressions

     AS YOU: • investigate rules of thumb
                 • work with algebra and rules of thumb

Exploration 1: Writing Equations

Writing Equations for Word Sentences

Word sentences can be expressed as equations using *variables*. A **variable** is a symbol used to represent a quantity that is unknown or that can change. Any quantity that does not change is a **constant**.

To write an equation, first choose a variable to represent each of the quantities that are unknown or that may change. Then use mathematical expressions to represent the word relationships between the quantities.

Example

Change the statement below into an equation. Tell what each variable represents.

The total cost for a family to join a local health club is $100 the first month and $47 for each month thereafter.

Then, find the cost for a family to use the health club for 1 year (12 months).

■ Sample Response ■

Step 1   Choose a variable to represent each of the unknowns.

Let c = the total cost and let m = the number of months (not including the first month).

Step 2   Represent the word relationships with symbols and variables.

$c = 100 + 47m$

Step 3   Substitute 11 for the variable m.

$c = 100 + 47(11)$
$ = 100 + 517$
$ = 617$

So, the total cost for a family to use the health club for a year is $617.

Name _____   Date _____

 **Study Guide**
For use with Section 3

Exploration 2: Solving Equations

To **solve an equation** means to find the **solution** of the equation, or the value of the variable that makes the equation true.

You can find a solution by using **inverse operations**. Inverse operations are operations that undo each other. Addition and subtraction are inverse operations. So are multiplication and division.

Example

Use inverse operations to solve $3x + 1 = 7$.

■ Sample Response ■

$$3x + 1 = 7$$
$$3x + 1 - 1 = 7 - 1 \qquad \leftarrow \text{The inverse of addition is subtraction.}$$
$$3x = 6 \qquad \leftarrow \text{Simplify.}$$
$$\frac{3x}{3} = \frac{6}{3} \qquad \leftarrow \text{The inverse of multiplication is division.}$$
$$x = 2 \qquad \leftarrow \text{Simplify.}$$

Exploration 3: Simplifying Expressions

Combining Like Terms

The parts of an expression that are added together are called **terms**. Terms with identical variable parts are called **like terms**. Like terms can be combined by adding or subtracting *coefficients*. A **coefficient** is the numeral part of the term.

Expression: $3y + 5 + 2y + 6 + y^3$

Terms: $3y$, 5, $2y$, 6, y^3

Like terms: $3y$ and $2y$; 5 and 6

Coefficients: 3, 5, 2, 6, and 1

To simplify some expressions and to solve some equations, you can combine like terms by adding and subtracting coefficients.

Name _____ Date _____

Study Guide
For use with Section 3

Example

Combine like terms to simplify the equation $4x + 4 + 5x + 9 = 22$. Then solve it.

■ Sample Response ■

On the left side of the equation, the like terms are $4x$ and $5x$, and 4 and 9.

$$4x + 4 + 5x + 9 = 22$$
$$(4x + 5x) + (4 + 9) = 22 \qquad \leftarrow \text{Group the like terms.}$$
$$9x + 13 = 22 \qquad \leftarrow \text{Combine the like terms.}$$
$$9x + 13 - 13 = 22 - 13 \qquad \leftarrow \text{The inverse of addition is subtraction.}$$
$$9x = 9 \qquad \leftarrow \text{Simplify.}$$
$$\frac{9x}{9} = \frac{9}{9} \qquad \leftarrow \text{The inverse of multiplication is division.}$$
$$x = 1 \qquad \leftarrow \text{Simplify.}$$

The Distributive Property

You can use the **distributive property** to combine like terms to simplify expressions and equations.

The distributive property of multiplication over addition says that for all numbers a, b, and c:

$$a(b + c) = ab + ac \quad \text{and} \quad ab + ac = a(b + c)$$

The distributive property of multiplication over subtraction says that for all numbers a, b, and c:

$$a(b - c) = ab - ac \quad \text{and} \quad ab - ac = a(b - c)$$

Example

Use the distributive property of multiplication over addition to simplify the expression $5(x + 3)$.

■ Sample Response ■

$$5(x + 3) = 5(x) + 5(3)$$
$$= 5x + 15$$

Name _____ Date _____

Study Guide: Practice & Application Exercises
For use with Section 3

Exploration 1

Use variables to write each word sentence as an equation. Tell what each variable represents.

1. Theresa just started her new job. She will earn $6.25 an hour.

2. The cost of going to the zoo is $4.50 for each adult and $2.50 for each child.

3. The total miles of a road trip divided by 60 gives the approximate number of hours the trip will take.

4. Kevin is making potato salad for a picnic. He will need 2 potatoes for each person invited.

5. The sewing club is making new outfits. They will need 2 yards of fabric for each shirt and 3 yards of fabric for each dress.

Exploration 2

Use inverse operations to solve each equation. Check your solutions.

6. $4m + 8 = 24$
7. $7h = 56$
8. $\frac{y}{13} = 9$
9. $3y + 12 = 36$
10. $5p - 6 = 19$
11. $7a = 21$
12. $\frac{m}{6} = 8$
13. $\frac{x}{3} + 1 = 10$
14. $\frac{t}{4} - 2 = 13$

Exploration 3

Combine like terms to simplify each expression.

15. $8m + 4m - 7$
16. $8 + 5ty - y + 4ty$
17. $\frac{1}{2} + 3w^2 - 4w$

Solve each equation. If possible, combine like terms to simplify each equation before solving.

18. $2x + 3 + 9 = 56$
19. $5y - y + 1 = 13$
20. $7t - 4t + 3 - 1 = 29$

21. Use the distributive property of multiplication over addition to simplify the expression $3h + 5 + 2h - 20$.

Name _____   Date _____

Quick Quiz
For use after Section 3

For Questions 1–2, use variables to write each word sentence as an equation. Tell what each variable represents.

1. To estimate the number of Calories you burn playing soccer for one hour, multiply your weight by 3.7.

2. The total money collected for the play will be $3 per student ticket plus $5 per adult ticket sold.

For Questions 3–5, use inverse operations to solve each equation. Check your solutions.

3. $\frac{x}{12} = 14$

4. $2y - 4 = 20$

5. $44 = 9 + 5m$

6. If possible, combine like terms to simplify each expression.

   a. $12x + 8 - 2x$

   b. $9x^2 + 6x + 8x^2$

Name _____ Date _____

Warm-Up Exercises
For use with Section 4

Use the table to write each pair of numbers as an ordered pair.

x	0	1	2	3	4	5
y	1	4	7	10	13	16

ANSWERS

(0, 1), (1, 4), (2, 7), (3, 10), (4, 13), (5, 16)

Name _____   Date _____

Correlations and Fitted Lines (Use with Question 15 on page 55.)

Directions Complete parts (a)–(c) for each scatter plot. Record answers to parts (a) and (b) in the blanks provided below each graph.

   a. Tell whether there is a *positive correlation*, a *negative correlation*, or *no correlation* between *x* and *y*.

   b. If there is a correlation, describe it as *strong* or *weak*.

   c. If the data points appear to fall along a line, draw a fitted line.

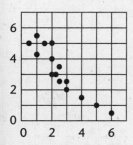

a. _____

b. _____

a. _____

b. _____

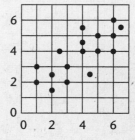

a. _____

b. _____

Name _____ Date _____

World Record Marathon Times (Use with Exercises 1–3 on pages 57–58.)

Directions Use the scatter plot below to compare record marathon times for men and women of different ages.

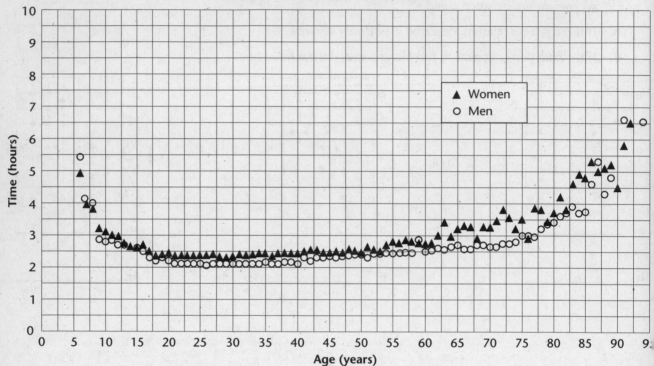

Record Marathon Times, 2004

Name _____ Date _____

Practice and Applications
For use with Section 4

For use with Exploration 1

The scatter plot for Exercises 1–2 shows the winning times for the men's and women's 200-Meter Butterfly swimming events in the 1968–1996 Olympic Games.

1. **a.** What is the approximate fastest winning time of the men's event?

   b. What is the approximate fastest winning time of the women's event?

2. **a.** In what years do the times seem to change very little for each group?

   b. Which group had the most change in the winning times?

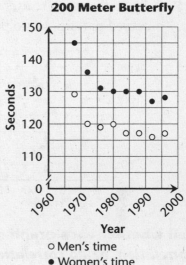

200 Meter Butterfly

○ Men's time
● Women's time

The table below shows the number of wins and the number of runs scored for the American League in 1996. Use the data set for Exercises 3–4.

	Wins	Runs		Wins	Runs		Wins	Runs
New York Yankees	92	871	Cleveland Indians	99	952	Texas Rangers	90	928
Baltimore Orioles	88	949	Chicago White Sox	85	898	Seattle Mariners	85	993
Boston Red Sox	85	928	Milwaukee Brewers	80	894	Oakland Athletics	78	861
Toronto Blue Jays	74	766	Minnesota Twins	78	877	California Angels	70	762
Detroit Tigers	53	783	Kansas City Royals	75	746			

3. Construct a scatter plot that compares wins with the number of runs scored. Put the number of runs scored on the horizontal axis.

4. **a.** Find the range for the number of runs scored. What is the greatest number of runs scored? the least?

   b. Does the number of runs scored seem to be related to the number of wins? Can this be expected? Explain your thinking.

(continued)

Practice and Applications

MODULE 1

For use with Section 4

For use with Exploration 2

5. Tell whether each scatter plot appears to have a straight-line pattern, a curved pattern, or no pattern.

a.

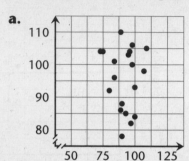

b.

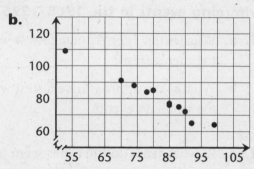

Tell whether each graph shows a *positive correlation*, a *negative correlation*, or *no correlation* between the two variables.

6. the graph in Exercise 5, part (a)

7. the graph in Exercise 5, part (b)

8. a. Draw a fitted line on your scatter plot for wins versus runs from Exercises 3 and 4.

    b. Does the line in the scatter plot in part (a) represent the data well? Explain what it shows about the runs scored compared to the wins.

    c. Use part (a) to determine what number of wins you would expect from a team that has scored 1050 runs.

The table represents record times in freestyle swimming for men and women.

9. a. Construct a scatter plot with men's time and the women's time on the same graph. Use a different mark or color for the women's plot.

    b. Describe the pattern you see in each scatter plot. Draw a fitted line for each if it makes sense.

    c. What can you conclude about the men's and women's time as the number of meters increases?

Meters	Men's time (seconds)	Women's time (seconds)
50	22	25
100	48	54
200	107	112
400	224	245
800	466	496

Name _____   Date _____

Study Guide
For use with Section 4

Athletic Triumphs   Scatter Plots

GOAL   **LEARN HOW TO:** • organize data in a scatter plot
• use a fitted line to make predictions

AS YOU: • analyze data about height, jumping distance, and
the Tour de France

Exploration 1: Making a Scatter Plot

Scatter Plots

A **scatter plot** is the graph of a set of data pairs. A scatter plot can help
you to recognize patterns and make predictions.

On a scatter plot, one set of data is modeled along the horizontal axis
and the other set is modeled along the vertical axis. The numbers
written along each axis are called its **scale**.

The range of each data set determines the scale of each axis of the scatter
plot. The numbers on the scale can increase by ones, but when the data
are spread over a large range it may be better to choose a scale that
increases by twos, fives, tens, or some other number.

The **interval** between lines is constant. It can be any convenient value.
The two axes can have different scales and intervals.

Example

The scatter plot below displays seed size and plant height data from the table.

Seed Size and Mature Plant Height

Seed Size (mm)	Mature Plant Height (cm)
3	101
4	107
5	115
6	175
7	280
8	375
9	423
11	475

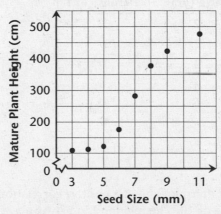

Seed Size and Mature Plant Height

The squiggle on the axis indicates that some of the scale has been omitted. The
horizontal axis has a scale that increases by intervals of 1. The vertical axis has a
scale that increases by intervals of 50.

Study Guide
For use with Section 4

Exploration 2: Fitting a Line

If the data points on a scatter plot appear to fall along a line, then a **fitted line** can be drawn to show the *pattern* in the data and help make *predictions*.

Correlation

Two variables that are related in some way are said to be correlated. There is a **positive correlation** if one variable tends to increase as the other increases. There is a **negative correlation** if one variable tends to decrease as the other increases.

Positive correlation   Negative correlation   No correlation

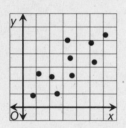   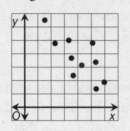   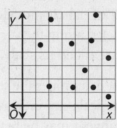

Example

Use the data in the table to make a scatter plot. Tell whether your graph shows a *positive correlation*, a *negative correlation*, or *no correlation* between the two variables. If it makes sense to do so, draw a fitted line for the data. Then describe the relationship and make a prediction based on it.

Age and Height of First 8 Children Seeing Dr. Smith on Tuesday

Age (yr)	Height (in.)
2	33
2	37
4	37
4	39
6	45
6	47
8	47
8	50

Age and Height of First 8 Children Seeing Dr. Smith on Tuesday

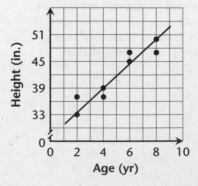

The scatter plot shows a positive correlation between age and height in children under the age of 10. The relationship between age and height in children under the age of 10 appears to be linear. From the scatter plot, you could predict that the height of a 7-year-old child would be about 47 in.

Name _____ Date _____

Study Guide: Practice & Application Exercises
For use with Section 4

Exploration 1

The scatter plot at the right shows the relationship between the high temperature and the number of ice cream cones sold between 2 P.M. and 3 P.M. each day during a two-week period.

1. What was the approximate temperature when the greatest number of cones was sold?

2. Suppose it is 2 P.M. and the temperature is 81°. How many ice cream cones can the owner expect to sell in the next hour?

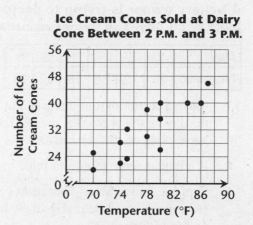

Ice Cream Cones Sold at Dairy Cone Between 2 P.M. and 3 P.M.

Exploration 2

3. The table shows the keyboarding speeds in words per minute (wpm) for 8 students. Make a scatter plot using the data. Put hours of practice on the horizontal axis. If it makes sense to draw a fitted line, do so.

Hours of practice	8	5	10	1	7	5	2	6
Speed (wpm)	45	35	60	18	45	33	25	40

Tell whether each graph shows a *positive correlation*, a *negative correlation*, or *no correlation* between the two variables.

4.

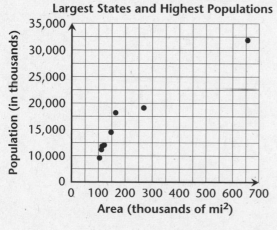

Largest States and Highest Populations

5.

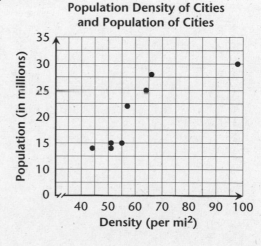

Population Density of Cities and Population of Cities

Name _____   Date _____

Quick Quiz

For use after Section 4

A bakery owner is trying to decide how many loaves of bread to bake each day. The owner records his sales for 14 days.

Day	1	2	3	4	5	6	7	8	9	10	11	12	13	14
Number	23	22	21	18	22	24	21	29	26	28	30	27	26	32

1. Make a scatter plot of the data. Put the number of the day on the horizontal axis and the number of loaves sold on the vertical axis.

2. If it makes sense to draw a fitted line, draw one.

3. Suppose 5 lb of bread flour makes 8 loaves of bread. How much bread flour should the baker plan to use on the 15th day?

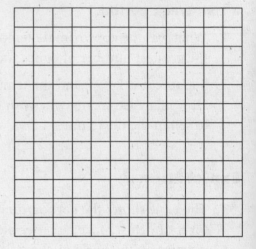

Tell whether there is a *positive correlation*, a *negative correlation*, or *no correlation* between the two variables.

4. height and hair color

5.

x	2	3	4	5
y	4	8	16	32

Name _____   Date _____

Warm-Up Exercises

For use with Section 5

Find the area and perimeter of each figure.

1. a rectangle with length 4 in. and width 7 in.

2. a square with sides of 3.1 ft

ANSWERS

1. $P = 22$ in., $A = 28$ in.^{2} 2. $P = 12.4$ ft, $A = 9.61$ ft^2

Name _____   Date _____

Rectangles with Area of 24 Square Units (Use with Questions 7–9 on page 65.)

Directions

a. On graph paper, draw 8 different rectangles that have an area of 24 square units.

b. Record the length, width, and perimeter of each rectangle in the table. Two rectangles have been done for you.

c. Use the data in the table to plot points for the width and perimeter of each rectangle on the coordinate grid.

Rectangles with Area of 24 Square Units								
Length	6	4						
Width	4	6						
Perimeter	20	20						

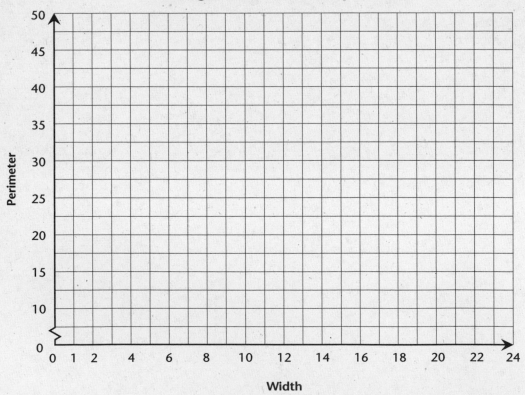

Rectangles with Area of 24 Square Units

Math Thematics, Book 3
Teacher's Resource Book, Modules 1 and 2

Name _____   Date _____

Rectangles with Area of 30 Square Units (Use with Exercise 4 on page 68.)

Directions

a. Complete the table of values for the lengths, the widths, and the perimeters of 8 different rectangles with area 30 square units.

b. Plot points for the width and perimeter of the rectangles on the coordinate plane.

c. Draw a smooth curve through the points.

Rectangles with Area of 30 Square Units								
Length								
Width								
Perimeter								

Rectangles with Area of 30 Square Units

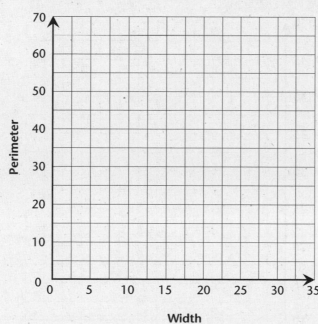

Name _____ Date _____

Rectangles with Perimeter of 28 Units (Use with Exercise 5 on page 68.)

Directions

a. Complete the table of values for the lengths and the areas of rectangles with a perimeter of 28 units and the given widths.

b. Plot points for the width and area of the rectangles on the coordinate plane.

c. Draw a smooth curve through the points.

Rectangles with Perimeter of 28 Units														
Width	0	1	2	3	4	5	6	7	8	9	10	11	12	13	14
Length															
Area															

Rectangles with Perimeter of 28 Units

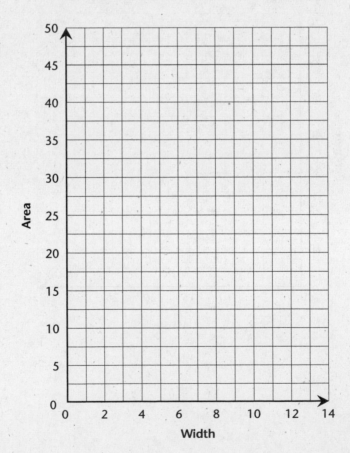

Name _____   Date _____

Polygon Dot Paper (Use with Standardized Testing on page 70.)

Directions Make a table that lists the area of each polygon and the number of dots inside and on the perimeter of each polygon. Then use the steps below to develop Pick's Formula.

Step 1 Divide the number of dots on the perimeter of the polygon by 2.

Step 2 Add the number of dots inside the polygon to your answer from Step 1.

Step 3 To find the area of any polygon, you always subtract the same number from your answer from Step 2. What is this number?

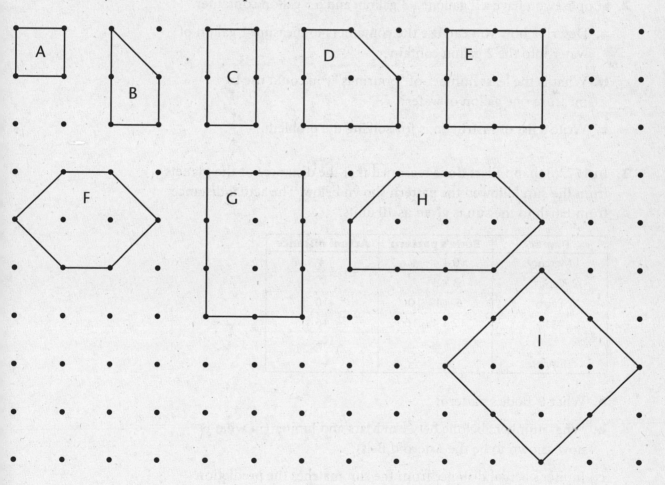

Name _____ Date _____

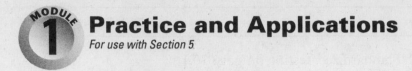

Practice and Applications
For use with Section 5

For use with Exploration 1

1. Suppose a gardener wants to estimate how many seedlings he can plant in a rectangular garden plot.

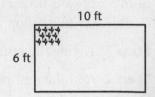

    a. Describe a strategy for solving the problem.

    b. Use your strategy to estimate how many seedlings should be planted in the garden at the right.

2. Suppose you have a 2 gallon, a 3 gallon, and a 5 gallon container.

    a. Describe how you can use the containers to measure 1 gallon of water into the 2 gallon container.

    b. What is the least number of "pourings" you could use to measure one gallon of water?

    c. Write a list of instructions for solving the problem.

3. In 1772, Johann Elert Bode reasoned that the distances of the planets from the sun followed the pattern shown below. The actual distance from Earth to the sun is given as 10 units.

Planet	Bode's pattern	Actual distance
Mercury	0 + 4 = 4	4
Venus	3 + 4 = 7	7
Earth	6 + 4 = 10	10
Mars	12 + 4 = 16	16
—	__ + __ = __	—
Jupiter	__ + __ = __	—

    a. What is Bode's pattern?

    b. What numbers belong between Mars and Jupiter (in what is now known to be the Asteroid Belt)?

    c. Jupiter's actual distance from the sun matches the prediction from Bode's pattern. What is the actual distance?

    d. Predict Bode's pattern for the next planet, Saturn.

Math Thematics, Book 3
Teacher's Resource Book, Modules 1 and 2

Name _____   Date _____

Study Guide
For use with Section 5

An Amazing Lake   Problem Solving and Mathematical Models

GOAL   **LEARN HOW TO:** • use a 4-step problem-solving approach
• use tables, graphs, and equations to model relationships
AS YOU: • learn about the Lake of the Ozarks

Exploration 1: A Problem-Solving Approach

Problem Solving

You can use this 4-step approach when solving problems:

Understand the Problem   *Identify* questions that need to be answered.
Find the information you need to answer them.
Restate the problem in your own words.

Make a Plan   *Choose* a problem solving strategy.

- act it out
- make a model
- make a picture or diagram
- make an organized list
- try a simpler problem

- examine a related problem
- use an equation
- guess and check
- work backward
- use logical reasoning

Decide what calculations, if any, are needed.

Carry Out the Plan   You may need to change your strategy or use a different approach, depending on how well your original plan works.

Look Back   Is your solution reasonable?
Is there another way you could have solved the problem?
Are there other problems you can solve the same way?

Mathematical Models

Tables, equations, and graphs can be used as mathematical models to study mathematical relationships.

Name _____   Date _____

Study Guide: Practice & Application Exercises

For use with Section 5

Exploration 1

Use the 4-step problem-solving approach.

1. Mark can do 50 sit-ups in 5 min. Describe a strategy for determining how many sit-ups he can do in 2 min. Use your strategy to solve the problem.

2. Marv and Gloria are in a band. They are performing a song in which Marv plays one note every 6 counts. Gloria plays one note every 10 counts. If there are 4 counts to a measure, in which measure will they both play together for the first time?

3. A pastry chef can use three different types of baking tins to bake muffins. They include 6-muffin, 12-muffin, and 18-muffin tins. Find a possible combination of tins to use to bake exactly 42 muffins in each situation.

   a. The 6-muffin tin is not used.

   b. At least one 12-muffin tin is used.

   c. Only one 6-muffin tin is used.

4. **a.** On graph paper, draw 6 different rectangles that have an area of 20 square units.

   b. Make a table of values for lengths, widths, and perimeters for these rectangles.

   c. On a graph, plot points for the width and the perimeter of the rectangles. Put width on the horizontal axis. Then draw a smooth curve through the points.

Use the table or graph you made in Exercise 4 to complete Exercises 5 and 6.

5. Estimate the width and length of a rectangle with the least perimeter. Explain how you found your answer.

6. What is the exact width of a rectangle with a perimeter of 24 units and a length of 10 units? Explain how you found your answer.

Name _____ Date _____

Quick Quiz
For use after Section 5

1. A drawer contains 4 black and 4 white socks. Two socks are removed in the dark.

   a. Describe a strategy for finding how many ways 2 socks can be selected from the 8 in the drawer.

   b. Use your strategy to find how many ways 2 socks that match can be selected.

2. Find the length of a rectangle with an area of 56 cm^2 and a width of $\frac{1}{4}$ cm.

Name _____ Date _____

Solution Guide: Textbook E²

For use with E² on textbook page 71

A Special Number

The Problem Solving, Connections, and Presentation Scales of the *Math Thematics Assessment Scales* are the ones most relevant to this problem. There is only one solution, but students' approaches to it will vary. Their solutions may include some of the following considerations.

Partial Solution

There are two solutions for 4-digit numbers that meet the requirements: 1210 and 2020.

Digit $\rightarrow$	0 1 2 3	0 1 2 3
Number of times $\rightarrow$ digit is used.	1 2 1 0	2 0 2 0
Sum of digits $\rightarrow$	$1 + 2 + 1 + 0 = 4$	$2 + 0 + 2 + 0 = 4$

In each solution, the sum of the digits is 4, the number of digits in the number.

Since each digit in the requested 10-digit number tells how often some digit appears in it, the sum of digits in the number must equal 10, the number of digits it contains. Once students notice the relationship between the sum of the digits and the number of place-value positions, they can list combinations of digits that have a sum of 10 and eliminate combinations until they find a solution, as shown on the next page.

(continued)

Math Thematics, Book 3
Teacher's Resource Book, Modules 1 and 2

Name _____   Date _____

Solution Guide: Textbook E²

For use with E² on textbook page 71

$9 + 1 + 0 + 0 + 0 + 0 + 0 + 0 + 0 + 0 = 10$ These can't be the digits because no digit appears 9 times.

$8 + 2 + 0 + 0 + 0 + 0 + 0 + 0 + 0 + 0 = 10$ These can't be the digits because no digit appears twice.

$8 + 1 + 1 + 0 + 0 + 0 + 0 + 0 + 0 + 0 = 10$ These can't be the digits because no digit appears 8 times.

$7 + 3 + 0 + 0 + 0 + 0 + 0 + 0 + 0 + 0 = 10$ These can't be the digits because no digit appears 3 times.

$7 + 2 + 1 + 0 + 0 + 0 + 0 + 0 + 0 + 0 = 10$ These can't be the digits because no digit appears twice.

$7 + 1 + 1 + 1 + 0 + 0 + 0 + 0 + 0 + 0 = 10$ These can't be the digits because no digit appears 7 times.

$6 + 4 + 0 + 0 + 0 + 0 + 0 + 0 + 0 + 0 = 10$ These can't be the digits because no digit appears 4 times.

$6 + 3 + 1 + 0 + 0 + 0 + 0 + 0 + 0 + 0 = 10$ These can't be the digits because no digit appears 3 times.

$6 + 2 + 2 + 0 + 0 + 0 + 0 + 0 + 0 + 0 = 10$ These can't be the digits because only the 2 appears twice.

$6 + 2 + 1 + 1 + 0 + 0 + 0 + 0 + 0 + 0 = 10$ This combination leads to a solution. There are six 0s, two 1s, one 2, and one 6 in the number 6210001000.

$6 + 1 + 1 + 1 + 1 + 0 + 0 + 0 + 0 + 0 = 10$ These can't be the digits because no digit appears 6 times.

This process can be continued to show that 6,210,001,000 is the only solution, but not all students should be expected to solve this portion of the E².

Name _____   Date _____

Format for an E² Solution
For use with Book 3

Include the following three main headings in the write-up of
your *E²* solution.

Problem Statement

Write out the problem in your own words.

Problem Solving Procedure

Include the following in this section of your write-up.

Work
- Show all of the work you did to solve the problem.
- Include any tables, charts, graphs, diagrams, models, drawings, or equations that helped you solve the problem.

Explanation
- Give a step-by-step explanation of what you did to solve the problem.
- Identify the problem solving strategies you used and explain why you chose them.
- Use correct mathematical vocabulary and symbols wherever they are needed.
- Explain any changes you made in your thinking.
- Explain why your answer makes sense.
- You may use tables, charts, graphs, diagrams, models, drawings, and equations to help explain your solution.
- Check your solution or verify it by solving the problem another way.

Connections
- Explain how this problem is like other problems you have solved.
- Explain how this problem relates to a real-world situation or another mathematical idea.
- Try to extend the solution to other problems that are like this one.
- Try to find a rule that will work for any case of the problem.

Conclusion

Include the following in this section of your write-up.

Answer
- Write your answer to the problem.
- Be sure you answered the question or questions in the problem and clearly described your solution.

Learning
- You may include more than one response.
- Summarize what you learned from solving the problem.

Math Thematics, Book 3
Teacher's Resource Book, Modules 1 and 2

Sample Scoring Profiles for an E² Solution

For use with Book 3

Excellent Response (A)

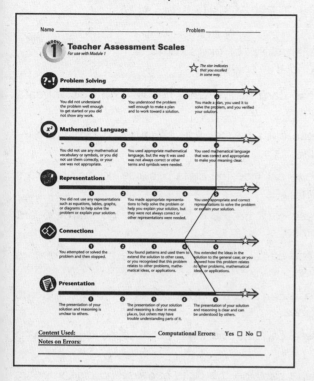

Good Response (B)

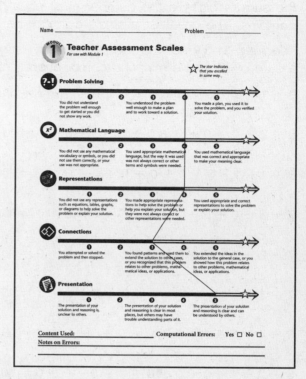

Developing Response (C)

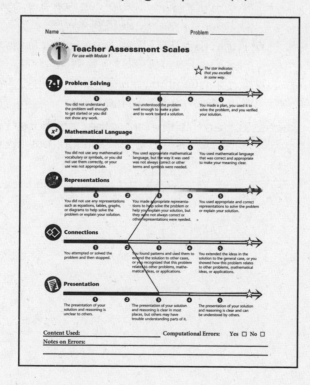

Name _____   Date _____

Student Sample 1: Matt's E² Solution
For use with Book 3

Since each digit in the number tells how often some digit appears in it, the sum of digits in the number must equal 10, the number of digits it contains. The greatest a single digit can be is 9.

I decided to try solving the problem by listing combinations of digits with a sum of 10 and eliminating combinations until I found the solutions.

$9 + 1 + 0 + 0 + 0 + 0 + 0 + 0 + 0 + 0 = 10$ These can't be the digits because no digit appears 9 times.

$8 + 2 + 0 + 0 + 0 + 0 + 0 + 0 + 0 + 0 = 10$ These can't be the digits because no digit appears twice.

$8 + 1 + 1 + 0 + 0 + 0 + 0 + 0 + 0 + 0 = 10$ These can't be the digits because no digit appears 8 times.

$7 + 3 + 0 + 0 + 0 + 0 + 0 + 0 + 0 + 0 = 10$ These can't be the digits because no digit appears 3 times.

$7 + 2 + 1 + 0 + 0 + 0 + 0 + 0 + 0 + 0 = 10$ These can't be the digits because no digit appears twice.

$7 + 1 + 1 + 1 + 0 + 0 + 0 + 0 + 0 + 0 = 10$ These can't be the digits because no digit appears 7 times.

$6 + 4 + 0 + 0 + 0 + 0 + 0 + 0 + 0 + 0 = 10$ These can't be the digits because no digit appears 4 times.

$6 + 3 + 1 + 0 + 0 + 0 + 0 + 0 + 0 + 0 = 10$ These can't be the digits because no digit appears 3 times.

$6 + 2 + 2 + 0 + 0 + 0 + 0 + 0 + 0 + 0 = 10$ These can't be the digits because only the 2 appears twice.

$6 + 2 + 1 + 1 + 0 + 0 + 0 + 0 + 0 + 0 = 10$ This combination leads to a solution. There are six 0s, two 1s, one 2, and one 6 in the number 6210001000.

$6 + 1 + 1 + 1 + 1 + 0 + 0 + 0 + 0 + 0 = 10$ These can't be the digits because no digit appears 6 times.

I tried to continue this process to see if there are other solutions, but it got too complicated. I think 6,210,001,000 is the only solution, but I'm not certain.

Student Sample 2: Linda's E² Solution

For use with Book 3

Problem Statement The problem is to find a 10-digit number in which the first digit is the number of 0s in the number, the second digit is the number of 1s, and so on to the units digit which is the number of 9s.

Problem Solving Approach If there are 9 zeros in the number, then there must be at least 1 nine, but then there are only 8 places for zeros, so there can't be 9 zeros.

0s	1s	2s	3s	4s	5s	6s	7s	8s	9s
9	—	—	—	—	—	—	—	—	1

If there are 8 zeros, then there must be 1 eight (There can't be more than 1 since the sum of the digits would be greater than 16. This also means there can't be more than one 6 or 7.) and at least 2 ones. But then the sum of the digits will be greater than 10 so there can't be 8 zeros.

0s	1s	2s	3s	4s	5s	6s	7s	8s	9s
8	2	—	—	—	—	—	—	1	—

If there are 7 zeros, then there must be 1 seven, 2 ones (There can't be more than 2 since the sum of the digits would be greater than 10) and at least 1 two. But then the sum of the digits will be greater than 10, so there can't be 7 zeros.

0s	1s	2s	3s	4s	5s	6s	7s	8s	9s
7	2	1	—	—	—	—	1	—	—

If there are 6 zeros, then there must be 1 six, 2 ones (There can't be more than 2 since the sum of the digits would be greater than 10) and 1 two. This is a solution.

0s	1s	2s	3s	4s	5s	6s	7s	8s	9s
6	2	1	0	0	0	1	0	0	0

If there are 5 zeros, there must be 1 five and zero 4s, 6s, 7s, 8s, and 9s otherwise the sum of the digits would be greater than 10. But then two of the missing digits must be a 2 and a 3, so the sum of the digits would be at least 11, so there can't be 5 zeros.

0s	1s	2s	3s	4s	5s	6s	7s	8s	9s
5	—	—	—	0	1	0	0	0	0

If there are 4 zeros, there must be 1 four and zero 6s, 7s, 8s, and 9s. But then three of the missing digits must be a 2, a 3, and a 5, so the sum of the digits would be at least 15, so there can't be 4 zeros.

0s	1s	2s	3s	4s	5s	6s	7s	8s	9s
4	—	—	—	1	—	0	0	0	0

If there are 3 zeros, a similar argument shows that the sum of the digits would be at least 21, so there can't be 3 zeros.

0s	1s	2s	3s	4s	5s	6s	7s	8s	9s
3	—	—	1	—	—	—	0	0	0

If there are 2 zeros, the sum of the digits would be at least 28, so there can't be 2 zeros.

0s	1s	2s	3s	4s	5s	6s	7s	8s	9s
2	—	1	—	—	—	—	—	0	0

If there is just 1 zero, the sum of the digits would be at least 36, so there can't be just 1 zero.

0s	1s	2s	3s	4s	5s	6s	7s	8s	9s
1	1	—	—	—	—	—	—	—	0

Conclusion Since there can't be 0 zeros, this shows that the only solution is 6,210,001,000.

Name _____ Date _____

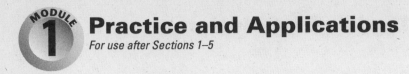

Practice and Applications
For use after Sections 1–5

For use with Section 1

Tell whether the given rates are equivalent.

1. 300 mi/hr; 50 mi/min

2. $9/hr; $0.15/min

3. 20 gal/km; 0.02 gal/m

4. 3 g/day; 0.021 kg/week

5. Use an equivalent rate to rewrite this statement so that it makes a more powerful impact: "A cricket chirps 10 times every 15 seconds when the temperature is 50°F."

Complete each equation.

6. 32 mi/hr = ___?___ mi/min

7. $0.13/in. = $ ___?___ /ft

Use the circle graph.

8. What percent of the students entering the science fair were sixth graders?

9. Without measuring, give the angle measure of the sector that represents students in the eighth grade entering the science fair.

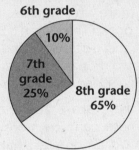

Science Fair Participants

For use with Section 2

10. Make a stem-and-leaf plot of the data shown below. Find the mean, the median, the mode, and the range of the data values.

325, 320, 300, 370, 270, 290, 320, 260, 270, 270, 250, 260, 240, 225, 250

11. The box-and-whisker plot models survey data from 25 classrooms. Find the lower extreme, the upper extreme, and the lower quartile of the data.

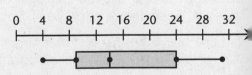

Students per Classroom Who Would Like to Study About Space

Choose a type of data display that you could use for each data set. Tell why you chose that type of display.

12. the amounts of snowfall during the days of a certain month

13. the percentages of people who shopped at The Corner Market, You Bag It, and The Food Place

(continued)

Math Thematics, Book 3
1-64 Teacher's Resource Book, Modules 1 and 2

Name _____   Date _____

Practice and Applications

For use after Sections 1–5

For use with Section 3

14. Use inverse operations to solve $2x + 3 = 9$. Then check your solution.

For Exercises 15–17, combine like terms to simplify each expression.

15. $15x - 3x + 9$

16. $m^3 - m^2 + 2mn + 3mn$

17. $8d - 5d + 3dr$

Solve each equation.

18. $\frac{x}{5} = 19$

19. $\frac{r}{20} + 3 = 8$

20. $9 = \frac{y}{24}$

For use with Section 4

Tell whether each graph shows a *positive correlation*, a *negative correlation*, or *no correlation* between the two variables.

21.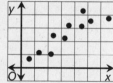

22.

For use with Section 5

Kevin is designing a garden for his backyard. He wants a garden space with an area of 30 square units.

23. On graph paper, draw 8 different rectangles that have an area of 30 square units.

24. Make a table for the lengths, widths, and perimeters of your 8 rectangles.

25. On a graph, plot the points for the width and perimeter of each rectangle. Put width on the horizontal axis and perimeter on the vertical axis. Draw a smooth curve to connect the points.

Use the table or graph you made in Exercises 24 and 25 to complete Exercises 26 and 27.

26. Estimate the width and length of a rectangle with the greatest perimeter. Explain how you found your answer.

27. What is the exact width of a rectangle with a perimeter of 22 units and a length of 6 units? Explain how you found your answer.

MODULE 1   **PROJECT LABSHEET** Ⓐ

Baseball Players' Life Spans
(Use with Project Questions 2 and 3 on page 73.)

Directions Use the data below to compare life spans of baseball players and prove or disprove a statement.

Life Spans of Major League Third Basemen and Shortstops (1920–1923 Season)

Shortstops' Life Spans (in years)

2	9
3	0
4	4
5	1 4 9
6	1 1 2 4 5 5 7
7	1 2 3 5 9
8	1 1 3 4 9
9	0 5

Third Basemens' Life Spans (in years)

2	9
3	1
4	0 3 9
5	
6	
7	2 4 4 5 7 7 7 8 9
8	1 3 4 4 5 5 7 7 8 8 9 9
9	1 2 3

2 | 9 represents a life span of 29 years.

Life Spans of Major League Third Basemen and Shortstops (1920–1923 Seasons)

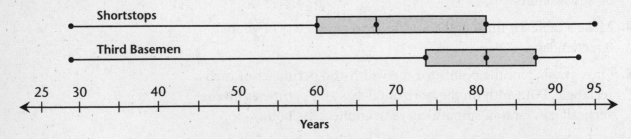

Name _____ Date _____

Test Form A

For use after Module 1

1. Some species of bamboo can grow at a rate of 21 in. per week.
   Write this as an equivalent rate in

   a. inches per day.   **b.** feet per week.   **c.** feet per year.

Two truck rental companies each have 12 trucks. The base cost to rent each truck for one day is shown in the table. Use the table for Questions 2–4.

8-Wheelers	42	42	45	49	49	56	58	66	72	78	78	78
Rent-a-Truck	40	45	48	49	49	49	57	62	62	68	68	70

2. **a.** Make a back-to-back stem-and-leaf plot that compares the base costs for the rental companies.

   b. Compare the shapes of the two stem-and-leaf plots.
   What do the shapes tell you about the costs of renting the trucks at the two companies?

   c. Find the mean, median, and mode for each data set.

   8-Wheelers: mean _____   median _____   mode _____

   Rent-a-Truck: mean _____   median _____   mode _____

3. The box-and-whisker plots below display the data from the table. Find the upper and lower extremes and the upper and lower quartiles for each box-and-whisker plot and record them in the table.

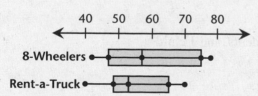

	Lower Extreme	Upper Extreme	Lower Quartile	Upper Quartile
8-Wheelers				
Rent-a-Truck				

4. **a.** Use the box-and-whisker plots to compare the prices of renting a truck from the two companies.

   b. How would the box-and-whisker plots above be helpful to a new truck rental company?

5. In a circle graph, one sector is to represent 40% of the students surveyed. Give the angle measure you would use to draw the sector.

Test Form A
For use after Module 1

6. Tell which type of data display would be best in each of the following situations.

    a. the tuition costs between $6000 and $10,000

    b. the age of each athlete who won a gold medal in the 2004 Olympics

7. Juwan drew 8 different rectangles, each with a perimeter of 20 in. He recorded the length and width of each rectangle and found the area. The data are shown in the table.

Length	Width	Area
9 in.	1 in.	9 in.^{2}
8 in.	2 in.	16 in.^{2}
7 in.	3 in.	21 in.^{2}
6 in.	4 in.	24 in.^{2}
5 in.	5 in.	25 in.^{2}
4 in.	6 in.	24 in.^{2}
3 in.	7 in.	21 in.^{2}
2 in.	8 in.	16 in.^{2}

    a. Use graph paper to make a scatter plot comparing length to area. Put length on the horizontal axis and area on the vertical axis.

    b. If there is a pattern, draw a curve connecting the points.

    c. Use your graph to estimate the length of the side of the rectangle with the greatest area.

8. Give an example of two variables that would have a negative correlation.

9. a. Admission to the school play is $3 for adults, $2 for students, and $1 for children under 6 years of age. Write an equation that represents the total cost of tickets for the play. Tell what each variable represents.

    b. How much would it cost a family of 2 adults, 3 students, and 1 child under 6 to go to the play?

10. If possible, combine like terms to simplify each expression.

    a. $xy + x$ **b.** $8y - 2y + y$ **c.** $6r - r + 2rt$ **d.** $g + 2gh - g$

11. Use inverse operations to solve each equation.

    a. $8y = 24$ **b.** $6 + 2x = 18$ **c.** $3r - 9 = 27$ **d.** $\frac{h}{6} = 7$

Name _____   Date _____

Test Form B
For use after Module 1

1. A racecar is travelling 90 mi/hr (1 mi = 5280 ft). Write this as an equivalent rate in

   a. miles per minute.   **b.** feet per minute.   **c.** feet per second.

Two car rental companies each have 12 types of cars. The base cost to rent each type of car for one day is shown in the table. Use the table for Questions 2–4.

Power Cars	22	22	24	26	27	27	32	44	44	44	52	65
Ignition Rentals	25	25	25	29	36	36	42	42	44	55	65	70

2. **a.** Make a back-to-back stem-and-leaf plot that compares the base costs for the rental companies.

   b. Compare the shapes of the two stem-and-leaf plots. What do the shapes tell you about the costs of renting the cars at the two companies?

   c. Find the mean, median, and mode for each data set.

   Power Cars: mean _____   median _____   mode _____

   Ignition Rentals: mean _____   median _____   mode _____

3. The box-and-whisker plots at the right display the data from the table. Find the upper and lower extremes and the upper and lower quartiles for each box-and-whisker plot and record them in the table.

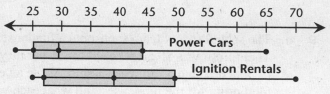

	Lower Extreme	Upper Extreme	Lower Quartile	Upper Quartile
Power Cars				
Ignition Rentals				

4. **a.** Use the box-and-whisker plots to compare the prices of renting a car from the two companies.

   b. How would the box-and-whisker plots above be helpful to a new car rental company?

5. In a circle graph, one sector is to represent 30% of the students surveyed. Give the angle measure you would use to draw the sector.

Name _____   Date _____

Test Form B
For use after Module 1

6. Tell which type of data display would be best in each of the following situations.

   a. the test grades of 20 students

   b. the salaries of 100 employees

7. Joann measured 8 rectangles, each of a different size. The perimeter of each rectangle was 36 cm. She measured the length and width of each rectangle. Then she found the area. The data are shown in the table.

Length	Width	Area
4 cm	14 cm	56 cm^2
5 cm	13 cm	65 cm^2
6 cm	12 cm	72 cm^2
7 cm	11 cm	77 cm^2
8 cm	10 cm	80 cm^2
9 cm	9 cm	81 cm^2
10 cm	8 cm	80 cm^2
12 cm	6 cm	72 cm^2

   a. Use graph paper to make a scatter plot comparing length to area. Put length on the horizontal axis and area on the vertical axis.

   b. If there is a pattern, draw a curve connecting the points.

   c. Use your graph to estimate the length of the side of the rectangle with the greatest area.

8. Give an example of two variables that would have a positive correlation.

9. a. The school soccer team sponsored a fundraiser to buy new equipment. Their profit was $0.50 for each candy bar they sold, $2.75 for each can of popcorn, and $3 for each T-shirt. Write an equation that represents the total profit for the fundraiser. Tell what each variable represents.

   b. How much profit would be earned on 350 candy bars, 82 cans of popcorn, and 41 T-shirts?

10. If possible, combine like terms to simplify each expression.

   a. $xz + z$ **b.** $7y - 2y + 4y$ **c.** $8r - r + 5rt$ **d.** $2g + 9gh - 2g$

11. Use inverse operations to solve each equation.

   a. $4y = 18$ **b.** $5 + 3x = 20$ **c.** $4y - 8 = 28$ **d.** $\dfrac{g}{8} = 4$

Name _____   Date _____

Standardized Test
For use after Module 1

---

1. It takes a jet airplane 4 hours and 20 minutes to travel nonstop from Chicago to Los Angeles, an air distance of 1745 miles. What is the average speed of the airplane?
  a. 436 mi/hr   **b.** 416 mi/hr
  c. 403 mi/hr   **d.** 388 mi/hr

6. Which type of display would best show the percent of students who received A's, B's, C's, and D's?
  a. histogram   **b.** line graph
  c. circle graph   **d.** scatter plot

---

2. Find the median of the data.

```
6 | 2 2 3 4 4 5 7
7 | 4 5 5 7 8 9
8 | 0 0 1 1 3 4 4 5
9 | 0 0 0 2 2 4 6
```

  a. 90   **b.** 80
  c. 79.5   **d.** 78.8

7. The following data represent the top ten countries with daily Calorie consumption over 3600 Calories. Which of the following cannot be an interval for a histogram of the data? 3847, 3815, 3779, 3732, 3708, 3681, 3669, 3664, 3634, 3633
  a. 3000–3500 Cal   **b.** 3600–3700 Cal
  c. 3775–3874 Cal   **d.** over 3800 Cal

---

3. Grasshoppers can jump 20 times their body length. Which equation represents this word sentence?
  a. $j = 20b$ **b.** $j = 20 + b$
  c. $j = 20 - b$ **d.** $b = \dfrac{20}{j}$

8. Combine like terms to simplify the expression $4xy + x - 2y - xy + 2x + 2y$.
  a. $3xy + 3x - 4y$ **b.** $6xy$
  c. $3xy + 3x$ **d.** $5xy + 3x + y$

---

4. The perimeter of a rectangle can be represented by the equation $P = 2l + 2w$. Solve for w when $P = 80$ cm and $l = 16$ cm.
  a. 64 cm   **b.** 12 cm
  c. 48 cm   **d.** 24 cm

9. Solve the equation $4y - 8 = 20$.
  a. 5   **b.** 7
  c. 24   **d.** 3

---

5. Which of the following is true?

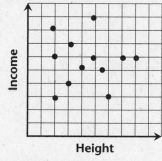

  I. no correlation
  II. positive correlation
  III. negative correlation
  a. I only   **b.** II only
  c. III only   **d.** not enough
                              information

10. What percent of students take American authors or comparative literature?

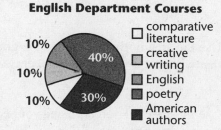

  a. 10%   **b.** 20%
  c. 30%   **d.** 40%

Name _____   Date _____

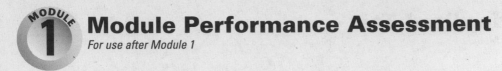

Module Performance Assessment

For use after Module 1

A cereal manufacturer needs a box with a volume of 3600 cm³. The dimensions for several possible boxes are given in the table below.

Boxes with a Volume of 3600 cm³								
Height (cm)	10	20	30	40	50	60	80	100
Area of base (cm²)	360	180	120	90	72	60	45	36

1. Is there a *positive correlation*, a *negative correlation*, or *no correlation* between the heights and the areas of the bases of the cereal boxes?

2. Use variables to write an equation that shows the relationship between the area of the base and the height of each cereal box. Tell what each variable represents.

3. a. Use graph paper to make a scatter plot of the data in the table. The horizontal axis should give the height of each box and the vertical axis should give the area of each base.

    b. If there is a pattern, draw a curve connecting the points and describe the pattern.

4. The cereal company gives away prizes to consumers who send in the top panel from their cereal box. To make it convenient for consumers, the manufacturer would like the box top to fit in a legal-sized envelope. These envelopes are about 10.5 cm by 24 cm. What dimensions would you suggest the manufacturer use for the box tops? Explain your thinking.

5. What is the area of the box top from Exercise 4?

6. Use the area in Exercise 5 and the graph in Exercise 3 to estimate the height that will give a volume of 3600 cm³.

7. Use the area in Exercise 5 and your equation from Exercise 2 to determine the height of the box.

8. Give the dimensions you would recommend for the cereal box. Justify your choice.

Contents

Book 3	Teacher's Resources for Module 2

At the Mall

Name _____   Date _____

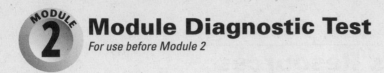

Module Diagnostic Test
For use before Module 2

Simplify each expression.   (Sec. 1)

1. $-15 + 17 =$ _____   **2.** $26 - (-12) =$ _____   **3.** $|-23| =$ _____

Evaluate each expression when *x* = –6.   (Sec. 1)

4. $-12x$ **5.** $\dfrac{36}{x}$ **6.** $4x$

7. Draw the triangle after the translation $(x - 3, y + 2)$.

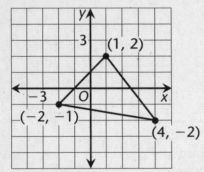

Find each sum or difference. Write your answers in lowest terms.   (Sec, 2)

8. $\dfrac{1}{2} + \left(-\dfrac{2}{3}\right)$ **9.** $\dfrac{11}{15} - \left(-\dfrac{2}{3}\right)$ **10.** $-2\dfrac{3}{4} - \left(1\dfrac{1}{6}\right)$

11. In a sack of 20 apples, 8 are golden, 8 are red, and 4 are green.   (Sec. 3)
    If 2 green apples are taken from the sack, what is the probability
    that the next apple taken is golden?

12. A coin is flipped three times.   (Sec. 3)

    a. Draw a tree diagram to show all the possible outcomes.

    b. What is the theoretical probability of the event "no tails"?

Math Thematics, Book 3
Teacher's Resource Book, Modules 1 and 2

Name _____ Date _____

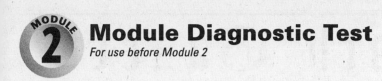

Module Diagnostic Test
For use before Module 2

13. Of 800 Midwestern teens surveyed, 59% said they watched music videos each day.   (Sec. 4)

   a. What was the sample? Do you think the sample is representative of all young people in the United States? Explain.

   b. Use mental math to find how many of the teens surveyed watched music videos each day.

14. Is the following question biased? If so, rewrite the question so that it is no longer biased.   (Sec. 4)

   "Do children spend too much time watching television?"

15. In a survey of boys and girls 12–14 years old, 48% of the girls and 72% of the boys said that pizza was their favorite food.   (Sec. 4)

   a. Suppose 580 girls were surveyed. How many of the girls said pizza was their favorite food?

   b. Suppose 814 boys answered that pizza was their favorite food. How many boys were surveyed?

16. A clothing store buys a pair of jeans for $24 and marks up the price to $39 for resale. Estimate the percent of the markup.   (Sec. 5)

17. A $74.50 item is discounted 40%. Estimate the sale price.   (Sec. 5)

The Math Gazette
At the Mall

Sneak Preview!

Over the next several weeks in our mathematics class, we will be practicing percent skills, learning about sampling and surveys, analyzing probabilities, and computing with integers and positive and negative fractions while completing a thematic unit entitled At the Mall. Some of the topics we will be discussing are:

▶ teenagers at shopping malls

▶ estimating percent of discount

▶ probabilities involved in store promotions

▶ video arcade games

▶ comparative shopping

Ask Your Student

How are video game characters programmed to move across the screen? (Sec. 1)

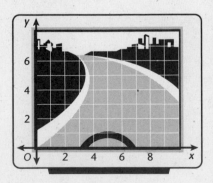

Suppose a coin is tossed twice. What is the probability that the result of both tosses will be the same, either both heads or both tails? (Sec. 3)

Which is the better bargain, 25% off the original price followed by an additional 10% discount or 10% off the original price with an additional 25% discount? (Sec. 5)

Connections

Social Studies:
Students will learn how to choose samples and conduct surveys. Discuss the importance of choosing appropriate samples and asking unambiguous questions.

Computer Programming:
Students will learn how a programmer makes figures move on the screen.

Literature:
Students can be encouraged to read *Hobie Hanson, Greatest Hero of the Mall*, by Jamie Gibson. The story is about a school in a mall. Discuss what it would be like to go to school in a mall.

E² Project

Following Section 3, students will have about one week to complete the Extended Exploration (E²), *Is It a Boy or a Girl?* Students will explore the probabilities of families of different sizes having children who are all boys or all girls.

Module Project

After completing the module, students will use the mathematics they have learned to create their own board games about shopping in a mall and share them with the class.

At the Mall

Section Title	Mathematics Students Will Be Learning	Activities
1: The Video Arcade	◆ adding, subtracting, multiplying, and dividing integers ◆ finding opposites and absolute values ◆ translating figures on a coordinate plane	◆ play the game *Integer Invasion* ◆ explore translations on a coordinate grid ◆ explore the graphs of linear equations
2: A World Class Wonder	◆ adding and subtracting positive and negative fractions ◆ adding and subtracting positive and negative mixed numbers	◆ play the game *Fraction Mindbender*
3: The Grand Giveaway	◆ finding experimental and theoretical probability ◆ recognizing equally likely, independent, and dependent events ◆ using tree diagrams to model the outcomes of an experiment and to find theoretical probabilities	◆ simulate the *Grand Giveaway* ◆ analyze promotional drawings ◆ play *Rock, Paper, Scissors*
4: Your Opinion Counts!	◆ estimating a percent of a number ◆ using proportions and equations to find percents and solve problems ◆ developing the meanings of population, sample, and representative sample ◆ summarizing and interpreting survey results	◆ conduct a survey about mall stores and mall visits and analyze the results ◆ make predictions based on samples ◆ identify biased questions
5: The Price Is Right, Isn't It?	◆ using estimation and mental math to find percents ◆ using percents to solve problems ◆ finding percent of increase or decrease	◆ play the game *Bargain Basement* ◆ compare sale prices

Activities to do at Home

◆ Describe the ways math is used in video games you have at home or you see in a video arcade. (After Sec. 1)

◆ Play *Rock, Paper, Scissors* with a family member. Find the experimental probability of each person winning. (After Sec. 3)

◆ Notice the types of advertisements in a newspaper sale insert. If percent discounts are advertised, estimate the sale prices. (After Sec. 5)

Related Topics

You may want to discuss these related topics with your student:

Mall construction

 Store promotions

 DEAL Misleading advertising

Name _____   Problem _____

Teacher Assessment Scales
For use with Module 2

☆ *The star indicates that you excelled in some way.*

 Problem Solving

❶ ❷ ❸ ❹ ❺ →☆

❶ You did not understand the problem well enough to get started or you did not show any work.

❸ You understood the problem well enough to make a plan and to work toward a solution.

❺ You made a plan, you used it to solve the problem, and you verified your solution.

 Mathematical Language

❶ ❷ ❸ ❹ ❺ →☆

❶ You did not use any mathematical vocabulary or symbols, or you did not use them correctly, or your use was not appropriate.

❸ You used appropriate mathematical language, but the way it was used was not always correct or other terms and symbols were needed.

❺ You used mathematical language that was correct and appropriate to make your meaning clear.

 Representations

❶ ❷ ❸ ❹ ❺ →☆

❶ You did not use any representations such as equations, tables, graphs, or diagrams to help solve the problem or explain your solution.

❸ You made appropriate representations to help solve the problem or help you explain your solution, but they were not always correct or other representations were needed.

❺ You used appropriate and correct representations to solve the problem or explain your solution.

 Connections

❶ ❷ ❸ ❹ ❺ →☆

❶ You attempted or solved the problem and then stopped.

❸ You found patterns and used them to extend the solution to other cases, or you recognized that this problem relates to other problems, mathematical ideas, or applications.

❺ You extended the ideas in the solution to the general case, or you showed how this problem relates to other problems, mathematical ideas, or applications.

 Presentation

❶ ❷ ❸ ❹ ❺ →☆

❶ The presentation of your solution and reasoning is unclear to others.

❸ The presentation of your solution and reasoning is clear in most places, but others may have trouble understanding parts of it.

❺ The presentation of your solution and reasoning is clear and can be understood by others.

Content Used: _____   Computational Errors: Yes ☐   No ☐

Notes on Errors: _____

_____

Name _____   Problem _____

MODULE 2

Student Self-Assessment Scales

For use with Module 2

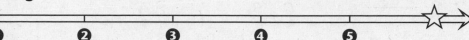

If your score is in the shaded area, explain why on the back of this sheet and stop.

☆ *The star indicates that you excelled in some way.*

 ## Problem Solving

❶   ❷   ❸   ❹   ❺ ☆

❶ I did not understand the problem well enough to get started or I did not show any work.

❸ I understood the problem well enough to make a plan and to work toward a solution.

❺ I made a plan, I used it to solve the problem, and I verified my solution.

 ## Mathematical Language

❶   ❷   ❸   ❹   ❺ ☆

❶ I did not use any mathematical vocabulary or symbols, or I did not use them correctly, or my use was not appropriate.

❸ I used appropriate mathematical language, but the way it was used was not always correct or other terms and symbols were needed.

❺ I used mathematical language that was correct and appropriate to make my meaning clear.

 ## Representations

❶   ❷   ❸   ❹   ❺ ☆

❶ I did not use any representations such as equations, tables, graphs, or diagrams to help solve the problem or explain my solution.

❸ I made appropriate representations to help solve the problem or help me explain my solution, but they were not always correct or other representations were needed.

❺ I used appropriate and correct representations to solve the problem or explain my solution.

 ## Connections

❶   ❷   ❸   ❹   ❺ ☆

❶ I attempted or solved the problem and then stopped.

❸ I found patterns and used them to extend the solution to other cases, or I recognized that this problem relates to other problems, mathematical ideas, or applications.

❺ I extended the ideas in the solution to the general case, or I showed how this problem relates to other problems, mathematical ideas, or applications.

 ## Presentation

❶   ❷   ❸   ❹   ❺ ☆

❶ The presentation of my solution and reasoning is unclear to others.

❸ The presentation of my solution and reasoning is clear in most places, but others may have trouble understanding parts of it.

❺ The presentation of my solution and reasoning is clear and can be understood by others.

Name _____   Date _____

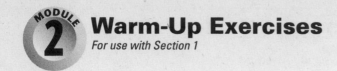

Give the coordinate of each point.

1. *A* _____

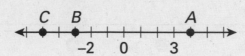

2. *B* _____

3. *C* _____

Match each set of coordinates with a point on the grid.

4. (3, 2)

5. (–2, 1)

6. (1, –3)

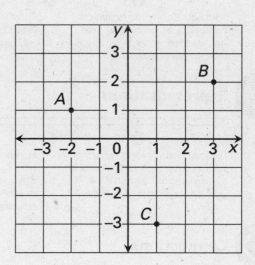

ANSWERS

1. 4   2. –3   3. –5   4. *B*   5. *A*   6. *C*

MODULE 2   **LABSHEET** 1A

Integer Invasion I (Use with the *Setting the Stage* and Questions 1–3 on page 78 and Questions 4–6 on page 79.)

Directions Read the rules below. Then play the game with a partner. Each player should make a *Recording Sheet* like the one below for recording his or her turns.

Game Rules:

- Players alternate turns. On your turn do the following.

  1. Roll the number cubes. The number on the blue cube is positive, and the one on the red cube is negative.

  2. To find the *x*-coordinate of your move, start at 0 on the horizontal axis. Move right the number of places indicated on the blue cube and left the number of places indicated on the red cube. This is the *x*-coordinate.

  3. To find the *y*-coordinate, roll the number cubes again. Start at 0 on the vertical axis. Move up the number indicated on the blue cube and down the number indicated on the red cube. This is the *y*-coordinate.

  4. Record the rolls and the coordinates on your *Recording Sheet*.

Example:

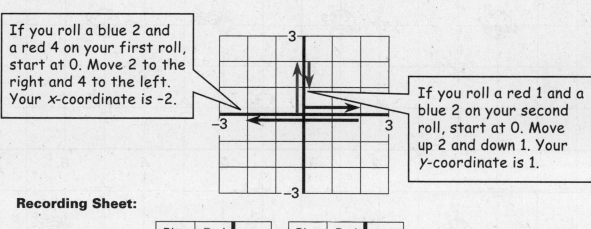

If you roll a blue 2 and a red 4 on your first roll, start at 0. Move 2 to the right and 4 to the left. Your *x*-coordinate is –2.

If you roll a red 1 and a blue 2 on your second roll, start at 0. Move up 2 and down 1. Your *y*-coordinate is 1.

Recording Sheet:

Record the two rolls and the coordinates.

Blue	Red	x
2	–4	–2

Blue	Red	y
2	–1	1

In this case, the coordinates are (–2, 1).

  5. Use the game board from Labsheet 1B. Place a disk on the point determined by your coordinates. If your disk is on a planet, a comet, or a star, you score the number of points shown on the game board. Otherwise you score 0 points. Return to the origin.

- Continue playing until your teacher says that time is up. The player with the most points wins.

Integer Invasion Game Board (Use with the *Setting the Stage* on page 78,
Questions 4–8 and 12 on pages 79–80, and Exercise 25 on page 88.)

Score Points: **Hit a star** **and score 20 points.**

Hit a planet **and score 30 points.**

Hit a comet **and score 50 points.**

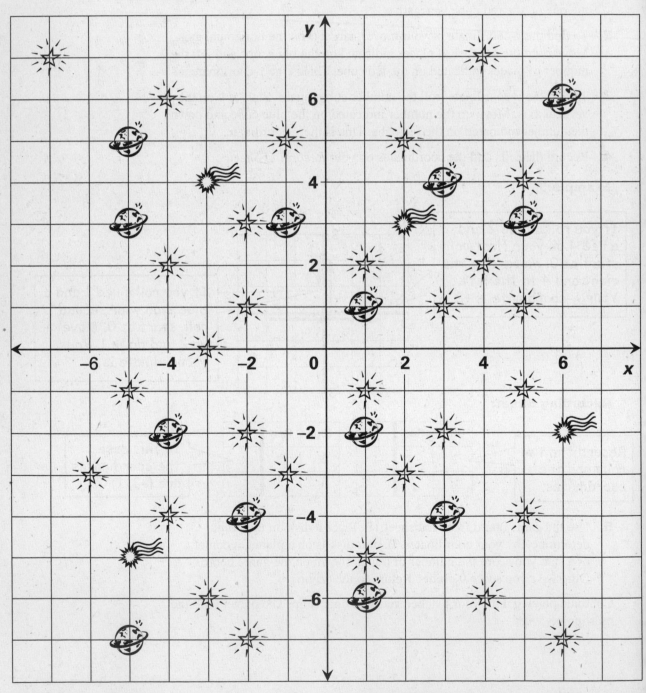

Name _____ Date _____

Exploring Translations (Use with Question 18 on page 81.)

Directions Draw a segment connecting each point (*A*, *B*, and *C*) to its image. Then answer the following questions.

a. How are the segments that you drew related to each other?

b. Trace the original figure. Slide the tracing along the segments until it fits exactly over the image.

c. Did you have to flip or turn the tracing in order to complete part (b)?

d. Compare the shape and size of the image and original figure. What do you notice?

e. Record the coordinates of points *A*, *B*, and *C* and of the image points *A'*, *B'*, and *C'* in the table below.

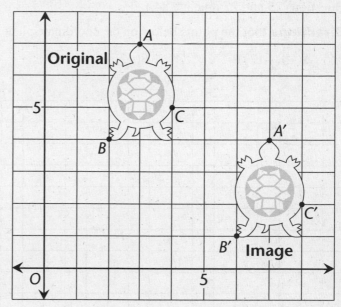

	Point	Coordinates	Point	Coordinates	Point	Coordinates
Original	*A*	(3, 7)	*B*		*C*	
Image	*A'*		*B'*		*C'*	

f. Let *x* represent the horizontal coordinate of the point. Write an addition expression using the variable *x* to represent the horizontal coordinate of the image of the point.

g. Let *y* represent the vertical coordinate of the point. Write a subtraction expression using the variable *y* to represent the vertical coordinate of the image of the point.

Name _____ Date _____

Exploring Multiplication (Use with Question 23 on page 83, and Questions 25 and 27 on page 84.)

Directions Plot the points below on the coordinate plane.

    $A(-4, -12)$ $B(-2, -6)$ $C(2, 6)$ $D(3, 9)$

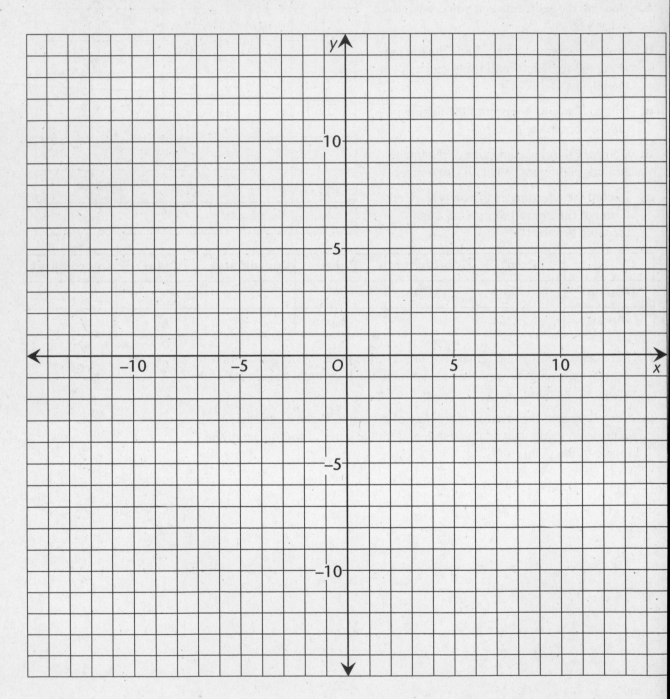

Math Thematics, Book 3
Teacher's Resource Book, Modules 1 and 2

Name _____ Date _____

Practice and Applications

For use with Section 1

For use with Exploration 1

Find each sum.

1. −19 + (−12)

2. 82 + (−8)

3. −12 + 5

4. 9 + (−9)

5. −72 + (−13)

6. 3 + (−12) + 8

Find the opposite of each integer.

7. −14

8. −92

9. 104

10. 17

11. −18

12. 3

Find each absolute value.

13. |14|

14. |−34|

15. |1|

16. |−3|

17. |41|

18. |−24|

19. Find two different integers with an absolute value of 13.

Solve each equation.

20. $|y| = 17$

21. $−x = −4$

22. $|s| = 0$

23. $−y = 6$

24. Huy earned $12 one week and bought a radio for $8. The next week he earned $5. He went to the mall and spent $2 on lunch. Write an addition expression for his earnings and expenses. Simplify the expression.

25. In which quadrant is triangle *ABC* located?

26. Give the coordinates of points *A*, *B*, and *C*.

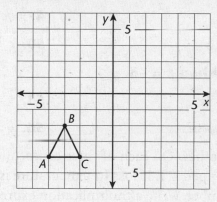

Find *y* when *x* = −7.

27. $y = 4 + x$

28. $y = x + (−3)$

29. $y = x + 2$

30. $y = 12 + x$

31. $y = x + (−9)$

32. $y = x + (−5)$

(continued)

Name _____   Date _____

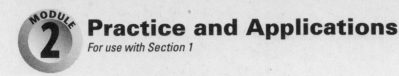

MODULE 2 **Practice and Applications**
For use with Section 1

For use with Exploration 2

Find each difference.

33. $9 - 12$ **34.** $12 - (-3)$ **35.** $3 - (-14)$

36. $-4 - (-4)$ **37.** $-18 - 3$ **38.** $-6 - (-21)$

39. The translation $(x - 3, y + 4)$ is applied to given figure *SHAPE*.

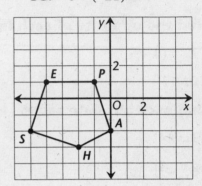

   a. Give the coordinates of the image points S', H', A', P', and E'.

   b. Writing Describe in words a translation that moves *SHAPE* to the opposite side of the vertical axis.

For use with Exploration 3

Find each product or quotient.

40. $-36 \div 12$ **41.** $\dfrac{-18}{-9}$ **42.** $-56 \div (-8)$

43. $\dfrac{-28}{7}$ **44.** $12 \cdot (5)$ **45.** $-23(-2)(4)$

Evaluate each expression when $a = -12$, $b = -4$, and $c = 32$.

46. ab **47.** bc **48.** abc

49. $a \div b$ **50.** $c \div b$ **51.** $a - b$

Find y when $x = -8$.

52. $y = 4x$ **53.** $y = -10x$ **54.** $y = 2x$

55. $y = -8x$ **56.** $y = 7x$ **57.** $y = -11x$

58. Weather On each of three consecutive hours, the temperature dropped 4°F. If loss in temperature is represented by a negative number, write a multiplication expression that describes the total change in temperature, and find the total drop in temperature.

Name _____   Date _____

The Video Arcade   Operations with Integers

GOAL **LEARN HOW TO:** • add, subtract, multiply, and divide integers
• find the opposite of an integer
• find absolute values
• translate figures
• define a translation algebraically

AS YOU: • simulate a video game
• explore translations on a coordinate grid
• explore linear equations

Exploration 1: Adding Integers

The **integers** are the numbers ..., –3, –2, –1, 0, 1, 2, 3, ... The sum of two integers may be positive, negative, or zero.

Example
Find each sum.
a. –5 + 4   **b.** 8 + (–8)   **c.** 5 + 5   **d.** –5 + (–9)
Sample Response
a. –5 + 4 = –1   **b.** 8 + (–8) = 0   **c.** 5 + 5 = 10   **d.** –5 + (–9) = –14

Absolute Value and Opposites

Two numbers are **opposites** if their sum is 0. For example, 6 and –6 are opposites. The **absolute value** of a number tells you its distance from 0 on a number line.

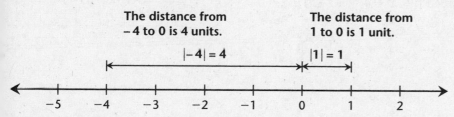

The distance from
– 4 to 0 is 4 units.

The distance from
1 to 0 is 1 unit.

$|-4| = 4$ $|1| = 1$

Coordinate Plane

The axes on a coordinate plane divide the grid into four sections or **quadrants**. They are numbered counterclockwise as shown.

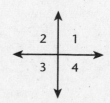

Study Guide
For use with Section 1

Exploration 2: Subtracting Integers

The difference of two numbers may be positive, negative, or zero.
To subtract an integer, add its opposite.

Example

Find each difference.

a. $4 - 6$ **b.** $-4 - 6$ **c.** $4 - (-6)$ **d.** $-4 - (-6)$

Sample Response

a. $4 - 6 = 4 + (-6)$
$\quad\quad\quad = -2$

b. $-4 - 6 = -4 + (-6)$
$\quad\quad\quad\quad = -10$

c. $4 - (-6) = 4 + 6$
$\quad\quad\quad\quad = 10$

d. $-4 - (-6) = -4 + 6$
$\quad\quad\quad\quad\quad = 2$

Translations

A **translation**, or slide, moves each point of a figure the same distance in the same direction. A translation can be described by adding values to the coordinates of a point. The result of a translation is the **image**.

In the figure at the right, the vertices of the original triangle, $\triangle ABC$, are $A(-6, 2)$, $B(-4, 4)$, and $C(-2, 3)$.

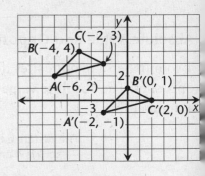

The vertices of the image triangle, $\triangle A'B'C'$, are $A'(-2, -1)$, $B'(0, 1)$, and $C'(2, 0)$.

This translation can be described by $(x + 4, y + (-3))$.

Math Thematics, Book 3
2-16   Teacher's Resource Book, Modules 1 and 2

Name _____   Date _____

Study Guide
For use with Section 1

Exploration 3: Multiplying and Dividing Integers

The product or quotient of two integers is:

• *positive* when both integers are positive or when both are negative.

• *negative* when one integer is positive and the other is negative.

Example

Find each product or quotient.

a. −4(−5)   **b.** 4(−5)   **c.** −20 ÷ 5   **d.** −20 ÷ (−5)

Sample Response

a. −4(−5) = 20   **b.** 4(−5) = −20   **c.** −20 ÷ 5 = −4   **d.** −20 ÷ (−5) = 4

Linear Equations

An equation whose graph is a straight line is a **linear equation**.

Example

The equation $y = x \div (-3)$ describes the relationship between x and y in the table below.

x	−9	−6	−3	0	3	6	9
y	3	2	1	0	−1	−2	−3

a. Plot the points from the table on a coordinate plane.

b. Is the equation $y = x \div (-3)$ a linear equation?

Sample Response

a.

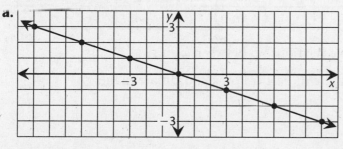

b. Yes, the equation is linear because its graph is a straight line.

Name _____ Date _____

 Study Guide: Practice & Application Exercises
For use with Section 1

Exploration 1

Find each sum.

   1. $-13 + 25$ **2.** $35 + (-15)$ **3.** $-5 + 8 + (-9)$ **4.** $-255 + (-22)$

Find each absolute value.

   5. $|45|$ **6.** $|-33|$ **7.** $|-2|$ **8.** $|12|$

Solve each equation.

   9. $|y| = 8$ **10.** $-x = -4$ **11.** $-w = 17$ **12.** $|z| = 22$

Exploration 2

Find each difference.

13. $-5 - 17$ **14.** $37 - (-6)$ **15.** $-27 - (-77)$ **16.** $-19 - 9$

17. After the translation $(x + 3, y + 1)$, the image of a point is $(10, 8)$. What are the coordinates of the original point?

18. Describe the translation below in two ways, one using only addition and one using only subtraction.

   Original   **Image**
   $A(-4, 5)$ $A'(0, 8)$

Exploration 3

Find each product or quotient.

19. $-6(-3)$ **20.** $6(-12)$ **21.** $-7 \cdot 8$ **22.** $-10 \cdot (-21)$

23. $-44 \div (-4)$ **24.** $-36 \div 9$ **25.** $\dfrac{45}{-5}$ **26.** $\dfrac{-220}{-10}$

27. a. Copy the table below. Look for patterns to find the missing values.

x	-4	-3	-2	-1	0	1	2	3	4
y	8	?	4	?	0	?	-4	-6	?

   b. What equation describes the relationship between x and y?

   c. Plot the points from your table in part (a) on a coordinate plane.

Name _____   Date _____

 **Quick Quiz**
For use after Section 1

Simplify each expression.

1. $-14 + 23 = $ _____

2. $34 - (-22) = $ _____

3. $|-14| = $ _____

Evaluate each expression when $x = -3$.

4. $-14x$

5. $\dfrac{36}{x}$

6. $24x$

Name _____   Date _____

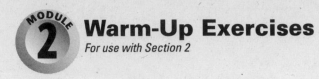

Warm-Up Exercises
For use with Section 2

Add or subtract.

1. $\dfrac{5}{4} - \dfrac{2}{4}$

2. $\dfrac{10}{12} + \dfrac{1}{6}$

3. $1\dfrac{5}{9} + 2\dfrac{4}{9}$

4. $\dfrac{16}{21} - \dfrac{16}{35}$

ANSWERS

1. $\dfrac{3}{4}$ 2. 1   3. 4   4. $\dfrac{32}{105}$

Math Thematics, Book 3
2-20 Teacher's Resource Book, Modules 1 and 2

MODULE 2   LABSHEET **2A**

Fraction Mindbender Game Boards
(Use with Questions 8, 9, and 11 on page 96.)

Player: _____   Player: _____

Game 1   ○ □/□ + ○ □/□   ○ □/□ − ○ □/□

Game 2   ○ □/□ − ○ □/□   ○ □/□ + ○ □/□

Game 3   ○ □/□ + ○ □/□   ○ □/□ − ○ □/□

Game 4   ○ □/□ − ○ □/□   ○ □/□ + ○ □/□

Game 5   ○ □/□ + ○ □/□   ○ □/□ − ○ □/□

Name _____ Date _____

For use with Exploration 1

Find each sum or difference.

1. $-\frac{6}{8} + \left(-\frac{5}{8}\right)$ **2.** $\frac{7}{9} - \frac{4}{9}$ **3.** $\frac{5}{9} + \frac{2}{7}$

4. $\frac{3}{4} - \frac{1}{6}$ **5.** $-\frac{8}{12} + \left(-\frac{1}{3}\right)$ **6.** $\frac{6}{10} + \frac{3}{5}$

7. $-\frac{5}{6} + \left(-\frac{1}{2}\right)$ **8.** $\frac{9}{15} - \frac{1}{5}$ **9.** $-\frac{4}{6} + \left(-\frac{3}{8}\right)$

10. $1\frac{2}{5} + 3\frac{3}{4}$ **11.** $5\frac{1}{6} + 2\frac{7}{9}$ **12.** $8\frac{3}{5} - 4\frac{1}{3}$

13. $9\frac{1}{10} - 4\frac{4}{5}$ **14.** $6\frac{3}{8} + 5\frac{3}{4}$ **15.** $7\frac{7}{12} - 1\frac{7}{24}$

16. $10\frac{1}{4} + 2\frac{5}{16}$ **17.** $11\frac{1}{2} - 5\frac{5}{8}$ **18.** $4\frac{3}{6} - 2\frac{4}{5}$

19. Cooking A baker has $18\frac{1}{2}$ pounds of flour and needs $1\frac{3}{4}$ pounds for bread for the week.

   a. After the bread is made, how much flour is left for other recipes?

   b. Is there enough flour to make seven batches of bread?

For use with Exploration 2

Find each sum or difference.

20. $-\frac{9}{5} + \frac{2}{5}$ **21.** $\frac{3}{8} - \left(-\frac{3}{4}\right)$ **22.** $\frac{9}{15} + \left(-\frac{2}{5}\right)$

23. $-\frac{5}{16} - \left(-\frac{7}{8}\right)$ **24.** $-\frac{4}{3} - \frac{5}{9}$ **25.** $-\frac{4}{9} - \left(-\frac{1}{3}\right)$

26. $-\frac{2}{5} - \frac{7}{15}$ **27.** $\frac{2}{9} + \left(-\frac{2}{3}\right)$ **28.** $-\frac{7}{10} - \left(-\frac{8}{15}\right)$

29. $-\frac{5}{8} - \frac{7}{9}$ **30.** $\frac{4}{5} + \left(-\frac{9}{10}\right)$ **31.** $-\frac{11}{15} - \left(-\frac{1}{5}\right)$

(continued)

Name _____ Date _____

Practice and Applications
For use with Section 2

For Exercises 32–34, find the fraction described by each set of clues.

32. The fraction is between -1 and 0. If you add $-\frac{1}{10}$ to it, the result is $-\frac{2}{5}$.

33. The fraction is between 0 and 1. If you subtract $\frac{4}{9}$ from it, the result is $-\frac{1}{3}$.

34. The fraction is between -1 and 0. If you add $-\frac{2}{8}$ to it, the result is $\frac{1}{12}$.

For use with Exploration 3

Find each sum or difference.

35. $2\frac{3}{4} - 3\frac{1}{4}$ **36.** $-2\frac{7}{8} + 5\frac{3}{4}$ **37.** $-1\frac{7}{8} - 5\frac{1}{4}$

38. $4\frac{1}{8} + \left(-3\frac{1}{6}\right)$ **39.** $-4\frac{3}{5} - \left(3\frac{1}{4}\right)$ **40.** $6\frac{1}{2} - \left(-2\frac{1}{4}\right)$

41. $-4\frac{2}{3} - 1\frac{5}{6}$ **42.** $7\frac{1}{4} - \left(-5\frac{3}{5}\right)$ **43.** $2\frac{1}{9} + \left(-6\frac{3}{6}\right)$

Challenge Solve each equation for *n*.

44. $-1\frac{2}{3} - n = 3\frac{1}{2}$ **45.** $6 = 4\frac{5}{6} - n$

46. Molly is making banana bread. The recipe calls for $1\frac{1}{2}$ c of mashed bananas. She has a total of $2\frac{2}{3}$ c of mashed bananas in a container.

    a. If she puts $1\frac{1}{2}$ c of the mashed bananas into her mixing bowl, how much will be left in the original container?

    b. Is there enough left in the container to make another batch of banana bread?

    c. If there is not enough left, how much more does Molly need if she wants to make another batch?

Study Guide
For use with Section 2

A World Class Wonder   Operations with Fractions

GOAL   **LEARN HOW TO:** • add and subtract positive and negative fractions
• add and subtract positive and negative mixed numbers

AS YOU: • play the game *Fraction Mindbender*

Exploration 1: Working with Fractions

Adding and Subtracting Positive Fractions and Mixed Numbers

To add and subtract positive fractions and mixed numbers, make sure that
the denominators of the fractions or mixed numbers are the same.

Example

Find each sum or difference.

a. $\frac{3}{7} + \frac{5}{6}$ **b.** $4\frac{3}{4} - 2\frac{1}{3}$

Sample Response

Begin by rewriting the fractions using a common denominator. Choosing the least
common denominator will usually result in an answer that does not have to be
reduced to lowest terms.

a. $\frac{3}{7} + \frac{5}{6} = \frac{18}{42} + \frac{35}{42}$ ← The least common denominator is 42.

$= \frac{18 + 35}{42}$

$= \frac{53}{42}$

$= 1\frac{11}{42}$

b. $4\frac{3}{4} - 2\frac{1}{3} = 4\frac{9}{12} - 2\frac{4}{12}$ ← The least common denominator is 12.

$= 2\frac{5}{12}$ ← Find the difference of the whole number and fractional
parts separately.

Adding Negative Fractions

To add two negative fractions, make sure the denominators of the
fractions are the same. Then use the same rules as for adding integers.

Name _____   Date _____

 **Study Guide**
For use with Section 2

Example

Find the sum. $-\frac{2}{4} + \left(-\frac{3}{16}\right)$

■ Sample Response ■

$-\frac{2}{4} + \left(-\frac{3}{16}\right) = -\frac{8}{16} + \left(-\frac{3}{16}\right)$ ← The least common denominator is 16.

$\qquad = \frac{-8 + (-3)}{16}$

$\qquad = -\frac{11}{16}$ ← Add the integers $-8 + (-3)$ to find the new numerator, -11.

Exploration 2: Fraction Mindbender

To add and subtract positive and negative fractions, use the same rules
as for adding and subtracting integers. Remember that subtracting is the
same as adding the opposite. Make sure that the denominators of the
fractions are the same before adding or subtracting.

Example

Find each sum or difference.

a. $\frac{3}{7} + \left(-\frac{5}{6}\right)$ **b.** $-\frac{3}{7} - \left(-\frac{5}{6}\right)$ **c.** $-\frac{3}{7} - \frac{5}{6}$

■ Sample Response ■

a. $\frac{3}{7} + \left(-\frac{5}{6}\right) = \frac{18}{42} + \left(-\frac{35}{42}\right)$ ← The least common denominator is 42.

$\qquad = \frac{18 + (-35)}{42}$ ← Assign the negative symbol to the numerator.

$\qquad = -\frac{17}{42}$

b. $-\frac{3}{7} - \left(-\frac{5}{6}\right) = -\frac{18}{42} - \left(-\frac{35}{42}\right)$

$\qquad = -\frac{18}{42} + \frac{35}{42}$ ← Add the opposite of the second fraction.

$\qquad = \frac{-18 + 35}{42}$ ← Assign the negative symbol to the numerator.

$\qquad = \frac{17}{42}$

(continued)

Study Guide
For use with Section 2

Sample Response (continued)

c. $-\dfrac{3}{7} - \dfrac{5}{6} = -\dfrac{18}{42} - \dfrac{35}{42}$

$\qquad = \dfrac{-18 - 35}{42}$ ← Assign the negative symbols to the numerator.

$\qquad = \dfrac{-53}{42}$ ← Subtract −35 from −18 to get the new numerator, −53.

$\qquad = -1\dfrac{11}{42}$

Exploration 3: Working with Mixed Numbers

Positive and negative mixed numbers can be added and subtracted just like positive and negative fractions once they are rewritten as fractions.

Example

Find each sum or difference.

a. $-4\dfrac{1}{5} + 2\dfrac{3}{10}$ **b.** $-2\dfrac{1}{3} - \left(-4\dfrac{2}{9}\right)$

Sample Response

a. $-4\dfrac{1}{5} + 2\dfrac{3}{10} = -\dfrac{21}{5} + \dfrac{23}{10}$ ← Rewrite mixed numbers as fractions.

$\qquad = -\dfrac{42}{10} + \dfrac{23}{10}$

$\qquad = \dfrac{-42 + 23}{10}$ ← Assign the negative symbol to the numerator.

$\qquad = \dfrac{-19}{10}$

$\qquad = -1\dfrac{9}{10}$

b. $-2\dfrac{1}{3} - \left(-4\dfrac{2}{9}\right) = -2\dfrac{1}{3} + 4\dfrac{2}{9}$ ← Rewrite as an equivalent addition expression.

$\qquad = -\dfrac{7}{3} + \dfrac{38}{9} = -\dfrac{21}{9} + \dfrac{38}{9}$

$\qquad = \dfrac{-21 + 38}{9}$ ← Assign the negative symbol to the numerator.

$\qquad = \dfrac{17}{9} = 1\dfrac{8}{9}$

Name _____ Date _____

Study Guide: Practice & Application Exercises
For use with Section 2

Exploration 1

For Exercises 1–6, find each sum or difference.

1. $\dfrac{7}{16} - \dfrac{3}{8}$

2. $\dfrac{7}{8} + 1\dfrac{1}{2}$

3. $-\dfrac{6}{9} + \left(-\dfrac{5}{12}\right)$

4. $-\dfrac{2}{7} + \left(-\dfrac{5}{7}\right)$

5. $-\dfrac{3}{4} + \left(-\dfrac{4}{5}\right)$

6. $6\dfrac{11}{12} - 3\dfrac{1}{3}$

Exploration 2

For Exercises 7–12, find each sum or difference.

7. $-\dfrac{1}{4} + \dfrac{1}{6}$

8. $\dfrac{2}{3} - \dfrac{4}{5}$

9. $\dfrac{1}{9} - \dfrac{2}{3}$

10. $-\dfrac{1}{6} - \left(-\dfrac{1}{6}\right)$

11. $\dfrac{7}{10} + \left(-\dfrac{11}{15}\right)$

12. $\dfrac{2}{8} - \dfrac{3}{4}$

Exploration 3

For Exercises 13–18, find each sum or difference.

13. $-1\dfrac{1}{3} - \left(-\dfrac{2}{9}\right)$

14. $-\dfrac{4}{5} + 2\dfrac{3}{10}$

15. $-1\dfrac{2}{5} - \left(-3\dfrac{4}{15}\right)$

16. $3 - \left(-2\dfrac{1}{2}\right)$

17. $5\dfrac{8}{9} + \left(-2\dfrac{2}{3}\right)$

18. $-1\dfrac{3}{6} - 2\dfrac{4}{9}$

19. a. Use the numbers 2, 4, 8, and 9, the symbols + and –, and the part of the game board shown to create the greatest number you can.

b. How would your answer to part (a) be different if both symbols were –?

Name _____ Date _____

 **Quick Quiz**

For use after Section 2

Find each sum or difference. Write your answers in lowest terms.

1. $-\dfrac{1}{2} - \dfrac{6}{16}$

2. $\dfrac{12}{15} + \left(-\dfrac{2}{3}\right)$

3. $-\dfrac{3}{4} - \left(-\dfrac{2}{5}\right)$

4. $6\dfrac{1}{3} - \dfrac{2}{4}$

5. $-2\dfrac{3}{8} + 5\dfrac{1}{12}$

6. $4\dfrac{5}{9} - 5\dfrac{2}{7}$

Math Thematics, Book 3
2-28 Teacher's Resource Book, Modules 1 and 2

Name _____ Date _____

Mid-Module Quiz
For use after Section 2

Evaluate each expression.

1. $34 - 49$

2. $134 + (-13)$

3. $12 - (-9)$

4. $-6 - 7$

Solve for _y_ when _x_ = –6.

5. $y = 6x$

6. $y = -9x$

7. $y = \dfrac{24}{x}$

Write each subtraction expression as an addition expression.

8. $6 - 13$

9. $-3 - 94$

10. $-13 - (-27)$

11. $18 - (-102)$

12. Draw the following figure after the translation $(x + 3, y - 2)$.

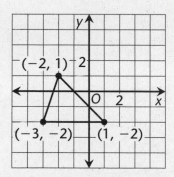

Find each sum or difference. Write your answers in lowest terms.

13. $-\dfrac{4}{7} + \left(-\dfrac{3}{4}\right)$

14. $1\dfrac{2}{9} - \left(-2\dfrac{1}{4}\right)$

15. $-\dfrac{3}{8} + \dfrac{2}{3}$

16. $4\dfrac{7}{10} + \left(-3\dfrac{5}{6}\right)$

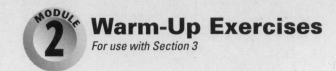

Warm-Up Exercises
For use with Section 3

Write each rate as a fraction.

1. 3 out of 7

2. 12 : 20

Write each fraction in lowest terms.

3. $\dfrac{55}{30}$

4. $\dfrac{9}{117}$

5. $\dfrac{16}{27}$

ANSWERS

1. $\dfrac{3}{7}$ 2. $\dfrac{12}{20}$ or $\dfrac{3}{5}$ 3. $\dfrac{11}{6}$ or $1\dfrac{5}{6}$ 4. $\dfrac{1}{13}$ 5. $\dfrac{16}{27}$

Name _____ Date _____

Grand Giveaway Experiment (Use with Questions 5 and 6 on pages 106 and 107.)

Directions

Grand Giveaway Spinner

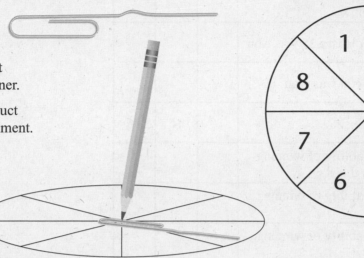

- Unfold a paperclip to use as a pointer for the spinner.

- When you spin the pointer, hold it in place with the tip of a pen or a pencil at the center of the spinner.

- Your group will conduct 16 trials of the experiment.

- A trial consists of spinning the *Grand Giveaway Spinner* 3 times. Since the first person in line has already spun the spinner, these are the second, third, and fourth spins.

- After each spin, record the value of the gift certificate won in the *Trials Table*. If the number is not a winner, write "Sorry" in the table.

Spin and Win $$$$$	
Spinner Number	**Gift Certificate Value**
1	$25
2	Sorry
3	$25
4	$10
5	$10
6	Sorry
7	$100
8	$10

Trials Table

	Spin		
	2nd	3rd	4th
Trial 1			
Trial 2			
Trial 3			
Trial 4			
Trial 5			
Trial 6			
Trial 7			
Trial 8			
Trial 9			
Trial 10			
Trial 11			
Trial 12			
Trial 13			
Trial 14			
Trial 15			
Trial 16			

MODULE 2   LABSHEET **3B**

Group Results Table (Use with Questions 6–8 on page 107.)

	Spin		
	2nd	3rd	4th
Number of times a gift certificate was won on this spin			
Number of times at least $25 was won			
Number of times $100 was won			
Total number of spins	16	16	16
Experimental probability of winning a gift certificate on this spin			
Experimental probability of winning at least $25			
Experimental probability of winning $100 on this spin			

Class Results Table (Use with Questions 9–11 on page 107.)

	Spin		
	2nd	3rd	4th
Number of times a gift certificate was won on this spin			
Number of times at least $25 was won			
Number of times $100 was won			
Total number of spins			
Experimental probability of winning a gift certificate on this spin			
Experimental probability of winning at least $25			
Experimental probability of winning $100 on this spin			

Math Thematics, Book 3
Teacher's Resource Book, Modules 1 and 2

MODULE 2   LABSHEET **3C**

Grand Prize Giveaway Tree Diagram
(Use with Questions 23–26 on pages 112–113.)

Directions Complete the tree diagram.

1st Draw	2nd Draw	3rd Draw	4th Draw	Outcome

Tree diagram with outcomes:

T → A → R → E : TARE
T → A → E → R : TAER
T → R → A → E : TRAE
T → R → E → A : TREA
T → E → R → A : TERA
T → E → A → R : TEAR
A → T → E → R : ATER
A → T → R → E : ATRE
A → R → E → T : ARET
A → R → T → E : ARTE
A → E → T → R : AETR
A → E → R → T : AERT
R → T → A → E : RTAE
R → T → E → A : RTEA
R → A → T → E : RATE
R → A → E → T : RAET
E → ...
E → T → ...
E → A → ...
E → R → ...

Name _____ Date _____

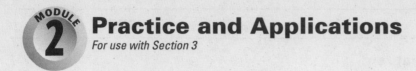

MODULE 2 Practice and Applications
For use with Section 3

For use with Exploration 1

In Exercises 1–3, tell whether or not the outcomes of the events described are equally likely.

1. "rolling an odd number on a cube with sides numbered 1 through 6" and "rolling a number that is evenly divisible by 3"

2. "rolling a number greater than 4 on a cube with sides numbered 1 through 6" and "rolling a number less than 2"

3. "spinning an A on this spinner" or "spinning a B on this spinner"

A game uses the spinner shown. Three players take turns spinning the spinner. If the spinner lands on A, Player 1 wins. If the spinner lands on B, Player 2 wins. If the spinner lands on C, Player 3 wins. If the spinner lands on D, nobody wins.

4. **a.** Play 20 rounds of the spinner game with two partners. After each round, record the results in the table like this one.

   b. What is the theoretical probability of Player 1 winning? of Player 2 winning? of Player 3 winning? of no player winning?

Round number	Player 1	Player 2	Player 3
1	W	L	L
2	L	W	L
3	L	L	L

   c. Did any player win most often? Do your results agree with the theoretical probabilities in part (b)?

For use with Exploration 2

For Exercises 5–8, a number cube with sides numbered 1 through 6 is rolled. Find each probability and plot the number on a number line. Label each point.

5. the theoretical probability of rolling a 5

6. the theoretical probability of rolling an 8

7. the theoretical probability of rolling a 2, 3, or 4

8. the theoretical probability of rolling a number less than 4

9. Which of the events in Exercises 5–8 are certain? Which are impossible?

(continued)

Math Thematics, Book 3
Teacher's Resource Book, Modules 1 and 2

Name _____ Date _____

Practice and Applications

For use with Section 3

10. In a bag of 50 marbles, 20 are red and 30 are green.

    a. One marble is drawn from the bag. What is the probability that it is a red marble? that it is *not* a red marble?

    b. Suppose the red marble is drawn at the first draw and not replaced. What is the probability of drawing a red marble on the second draw?

    c. Suppose a green marble is drawn on the first draw and not replaced. What is the probability of drawing a red marble on the second draw?

    d. Is drawing a red marble on the second draw *dependent on* the first draw or *independent of* the first draw? Explain your answer.

    e. Suppose a red marble is drawn on the first draw and replaced. What is the probability that a red marble is drawn on the next draw? Compare your answer with your answer in part (d).

For use with Exploration 3

11. You are deciding between three pairs of pants and two sweaters. Draw a tree diagram to show the possible outcomes of choosing one pair of pants and one sweater.

12. The letters C, A, and T are written on separate identical slips of paper and placed in a bag. The tree diagram shows the possible outcomes for drawing the letters from the bag one at a time.

    a. Based on the tree diagram, what is the theoretical probability of drawing the letters in the order C-A-T?

    b. Based on the tree diagram, what is the theoretical probability that the final letter drawn will be C?

1st Draw	2nd Draw	3rd Draw
C	A	T
	T	A
A	C	T
	T	C
T	C	A
	A	C

13. Draw a tree diagram to show all possible outcomes when a coin is flipped four times.

Name _____ Date _____

Study Guide
For use with Section 3

The Grand Giveaway   Exploring Probability

GOAL   **LEARN HOW TO:** • find experimental probabilities
• find theoretical probabilities
• recognize dependent and independent events
• use a tree diagram to model and find theoretical probabilities

AS YOU: • simulate, examine, and analyze a promotional drawing

Exploration 1: Experimental Probability

Outcomes and Events

An **experiment** is an activity whose results can be observed and recorded. The result of an experiment is an **outcome**. Outcomes are **equally likely** if they have the same chance of occurring. An **event** is a set of outcomes of an experiment.

Example

Suppose an experiment involves rolling a cube numbered 1 through 6.

a. Name the possible outcomes and tell if they are equally likely.

b. Name some possible events.

Sample Response

a. The possible outcomes are 1, 2, 3, 4, 5, and 6. The outcomes are equally likely because they each have the same chance of occurring.

b. Some possible events are: rolling an even number; rolling an odd number; and rolling a multiple of 3.

Experimental Probability

A **probability** is a number from 0 through 1 that tells how likely something is to happen.

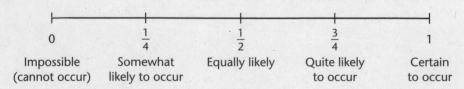

Probability

| 0 | $\frac{1}{4}$ | $\frac{1}{2}$ | $\frac{3}{4}$ | 1 |

Impossible   Somewhat   Equally likely   Quite likely   Certain
(cannot occur)   likely to occur   to occur   to occur

Name _____   Date _____

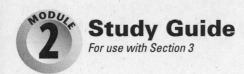

Study Guide
For use with Section 3

A probability that is found by repeating an experiment several times and recording the results is an **experimental probability**.

Experimental probability $= \dfrac{\text{number of times an event occurs}}{\text{number of times the experiment is done}}$

Exploration 2: Theoretical Probability

A **theoretical probability** is found without doing an experiment. When all of the outcomes are equally likely to occur, you can use this ratio:

Theoretical probability $= \dfrac{\text{number of outcomes that make up the event}}{\text{total number of possible outcomes}}$

Example

What is the theoretical probability of rolling a 1 on the number cube discussed in the Example on the previous page?

■ Sample Response ■

There are six possible outcomes, each of which is equally likely. Only one of these outcomes is a 1. So, the theoretical probability of rolling a 1 is $\dfrac{1}{6}$.

When the occurrence of one event affects the probability of the occurrence of another event, the events are **dependent**. Otherwise, they are **independent**. An event that cannot occur is an **impossible** event. An event that must occur is a **certain** event.

Exploration 3: Tree Diagrams

A **tree diagram** can be used to show all the possible outcomes of an experiment. You can follow a path along the "branches" of a tree diagram to examine a specific outcome. For example, the tree diagram below shows the possible outcomes of spinning the spinner at the right.

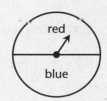

First Spin	Second Spin	Outcome
r	r	rr
	b	rb
b	r	br
	b	bb

The probability of spinning red once and blue once is $\dfrac{1}{2}$.

The probability of spinning the same color on both spins is also $\dfrac{1}{2}$.

Name _____   Date _____

Study Guide: Practice & Application Exercises
For use with Section 3

Exploration 1

1. The table at the right shows the results of 30 flips of a coin. What is the experimental probability of the coin landing on heads?

Heads	Tails
18	12

For Exercises 2–3, tell whether the events are equally likely.

2. "picking a red marble out of a bag with 3 red marbles and 3 blue marbles" and "picking a blue marble out of the same bag"

3. "rolling an even number on a number cube with sides numbered 1 through 6" and "rolling a 4 using the same number cube"

Exploration 2

In Exercises 4–7, suppose you spin a spinner that has five equal sectors numbered 1 through 5. Find the theoretical probability of each event.

4. spinning a 3

5. spinning a 1 or a 5

6. spinning a number greater than 5

7. spinning an odd number

8. In a box of 20 pencils, 10 pencils are red, 4 pencils are yellow, and the rest are blue.

    a. One pencil is taken from the box without looking. What is the probability that it is a red pencil? that it is not a yellow pencil?

    b. Suppose two pencils are drawn, one at a time. Are the two events below *dependent* or *independent*? Explain.

        Event 1: A blue pencil is drawn and is not put back in the box.

        Event 2: When a second pencil is drawn, it is also blue.

Exploration 3

9. a. Draw a tree diagram to show all the possible outcomes of two spins of the spinner at the right.

    b. How many outcomes are there?

    c. What outcomes make up the event "spins have a sum of 4"?

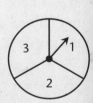

Math Thematics, Book 3
Teacher's Resource Book, Modules 1 and 2

2-38

Name _____   Date _____

Quick Quiz
For use after Section 3

For Questions 1–2, a cube with sides numbered 1 through 6 is rolled.

1. Find the probability of rolling an even number.

2. What is the theoretical probability of rolling a 6?

3. In a bag with 20 marbles, 5 are red. Suppose a red marble is drawn on the first draw and not replaced. What is the probability of drawing red on the second draw?

4. The tree diagram shows all possible outcomes when a coin is flipped three times. Find the theoretical probability of the event "no tails".

1st   2nd   3rd
Flip   Flip   Flip   Outcomes

```
              H      HHH
          H
              T      HHT
      H
              H      HTH
          T
              T      HTT

              H      THH
          H
              T      THT
      T
              H      TTH
          T
              T      TTT
```

Name _____   Date _____

Is It a Boy or a Girl?

All of the *Math Thematics Assessment Scales* should be used to assess student work. Expect most students to use a tree diagram or an organized list to find the probabilities. In either case, students will want to find a pattern before they reach a family size of five children.

The sample response below shows part of a student's solution.

Partial Solution

My tree diagram at the right shows the possible outcomes (gender) for 1, 2, 3, or 4 children in a family. In my diagram, B represents a boy and G represents a girl. You can use the tree diagram to find the probability that a family with one child has all children the same gender. This is shown in the first column of outcomes.

I thought a table would help me see the probability patterns better, so I organized my results in the table at the bottom of the page. I saw that for any number of children the probability that all the children will be the same gender is $\frac{2}{2^n}$. The O'Neils had a $\frac{2}{2^{10}} = \frac{2}{1024} \approx \frac{1}{500}$ chance of having 10 girls or 10 boys in a row.

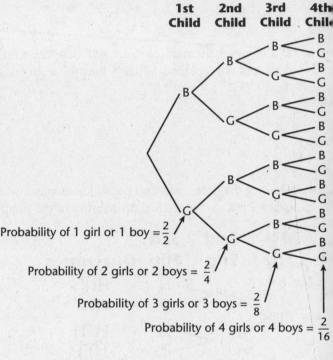

Probability of 1 girl or 1 boy = $\frac{2}{2}$

Probability of 2 girls or 2 boys = $\frac{2}{4}$

Probability of 3 girls or 3 boys = $\frac{2}{8}$

Probability of 4 girls or 4 boys = $\frac{2}{16}$

Number of children in the family	1	2	3	4	5	10	...	n
Probability they are all the same gender	$\frac{2}{2} = \frac{2}{2^1} = 1$	$\frac{2}{4} = \frac{2}{2^2} = \frac{1}{2}$	$\frac{2}{8} = \frac{2}{2^3} = \frac{1}{4}$	$\frac{2}{16} = \frac{2}{2^4} = \frac{1}{8}$	$\frac{2}{32} = \frac{2}{2^5} = \frac{1}{16}$	$\frac{2}{2^{10}} \approx \frac{1}{500}$	...	$\frac{2}{2^n}$

Other Considerations

- **Connections** Some students may recognize that the general rule could be written:

  Probability that all children are the same gender = $\frac{1}{2^{n-1}}$, where *n* represents the number of children in the family.

Name _____   Date _____

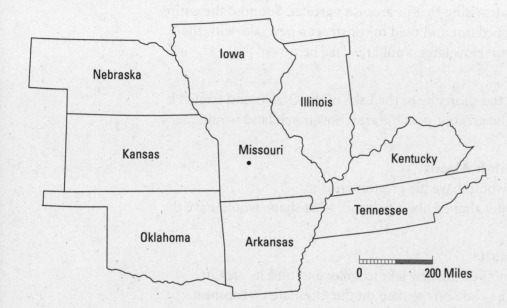

Name _____   Date _____

The Amazing Lake Revisited

Set Up
You will need the Alternate E^2 Labsheet.

The Situation
The shoreline of the Lake of the Ozarks is about 1300 miles long, but the lake's area is only 61,000 acres or about 95 mi^2. Since the shoreline is so long, it may seem surprising that its area isn't greater. Suppose the entire shoreline was stretched out and used to construct a new lake with the greatest possible area. How large would the lake be?

The Problem
If you were to take the shoreline of the Lake of the Ozarks and stretch it out so it enclosed the greatest possible area, how much land would the new lake cover?

Something to Think About
- What polygon would have the greatest area?
- If the lake was not shaped like a polygon, what shape would have the greatest area?

Present Your Results
Give the dimension(s) of the new lake in miles and find its area in square miles. Use the scale on the map on the Alternate E^2 Labsheet. Draw an outline of the new lake on the map. The dot on the map represents the center of the lake. What do you observe?

Name _____   Date _____

Solution Guide: Alternate E²
For use with Module 2

The Amazing Lake Revisited

There is only one solution to this problem, but students' approaches to it will vary. All of the *Math Thematics Assessment Scales* can be used to assess students' solutions.

The sample response below shows part of a student's solution.

Partial Solution

I started by trying to find the rectangle that has the greatest area when its perimeter is 1300 mi. I made a table and graphed the data to do this. Let L = length of the rectangle in miles, W = its width in miles, and A = its area in square miles.

perimeter = 1300
$2L + 2W = 1300$
$L + W = 650$
$L = 650 - W$

W	L = 650 – W	A = L · W
0	650	0
100	550	55,000
150	500	75,000
200	450	90,000
250	400	100,000
300	350	105,000
350	300	105,000
400	250	100,000
450	200	90,000
500	150	75,000

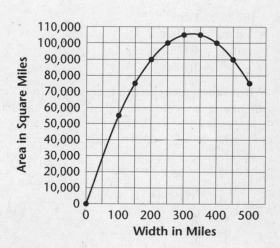

From the graph, I concluded that a square with a side 325 mi long would have the greatest area of any of the rectangles. The area would be about 106,000 mi².

Since a square is a regular polygon, I decided to see what the area would be if the lake was in the shape of a regular octagon. The length of a side of a regular octagon with a perimeter of 1300 mi would be $1300 \div 8 = 162.5$ mi.

Area of Trapezoid $= \frac{1}{2}(4.8 + 2)\,1.4$
$\qquad\qquad\qquad = 4.76$ cm²

Area of Rectangle $= 4.8 \cdot 2$
$\qquad\qquad\qquad = 9.6$ cm²

Area of Octagon $= 2 \cdot 4.76 + 9.6$
$\qquad\qquad\qquad = 19.12$ cm²

$\qquad 4$ cm² $= (162.5$ mi$)^2$
$\qquad 4$ cm² $= 26,406.25$ mi²
$\qquad 1$ cm² $= 26,406.25$ mi² $\div 4$
$\qquad 1$ cm² $= 6601.5625$ mi²
$\quad 19.12$ cm² $= 19.12 \cdot 6601.5625$ mi²
$\quad 19.12$ cm² $= 126,222$ mi²

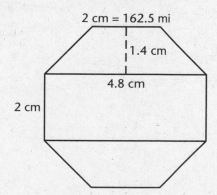

2 cm = 162.5 mi

1.4 cm

4.8 cm

2 cm

Solution Guide: Alternate E²
For use with Module 2

The area of the regular octagon is greater than the area of the square, and I think that as you keep adding more sides, the area of the regular polygon will keep getting bigger. So a lake in the shape of a circle should have the greatest area.

$$\pi d = C$$
$$\pi d = 1300$$
$$d = 1300 \div \pi$$
$$d = 413.8 \text{ mi}$$
$$\text{Area} = \pi(413.8 \div 2)^2$$
$$\text{Area} = \pi(206.9)^2$$
$$= 134{,}484 \text{ mi}^2 \text{ which is greater than } 126{,}222 \text{ mi}^2$$

$$100 \text{ mi} = 1 \text{ cm}$$
$$413.8 \text{ mi} = 4.138 \text{ cm}$$
$$\text{radius} = 4.138 \text{ cm} \div 2$$
$$\approx 2.1 \text{ cm}$$

When I drew a circle with radius equal to 2.1 cm on the map, I discovered that the new lake would cover all of Missouri and parts of the 6 surrounding states.

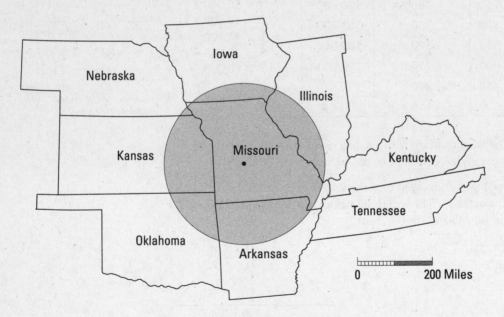

Name _____ Date _____

Warm-Up Exercises

For use with Section 4

1. Write 26% as a fraction and as a decimal.

2. Write $1\frac{2}{25}$ as a percent and as a decimal.

3. Write 0.09 as a percent and as a fraction.

Solve each proportion.

4. $\dfrac{x}{15} = \dfrac{16}{25}$

5. $\dfrac{14}{6} = \dfrac{y}{9}$

ANSWERS

1. $\frac{26}{100}$ or $\frac{13}{50}$, 0.26   2. 108%, 1.08   3. 9%, $\frac{9}{100}$ 4. 9.6   5. 21

Name _____   Date _____

Group Survey Results (Use with Questions 3–5 on pages 123–124,
Question 19 on page 129, and Question 21 on page 130.)

What kind of store do you think is most important at a mall? (Choose only one.)	Number of group members who chose the type of store	Ratio of the number of group members who chose that kind of store to the total number of group members		
		Fraction form	Decimal form	Percent form
A. clothing				
B. shoes				
C. CD/tape/video/music				
D. sporting goods				
E. department store				
F. video arcade				

How often do you go to a mall?	Number of group members who go that often	Ratio of the number of group members who go that often to the total number of group members		
		Fraction form	Decimal form	Percent form
A. one or more times a week				
B. once every 2 to 3 weeks				
C. once a month				
D. less than once a month				
E. never				

Name _____ Date _____

Combined Group Survey Results (Use with Question 21 on page 130 and Questions 23–26 on pages 130–131.)

Directions Combine your group's data from Labsheet 4A with data from two other groups. First record the total number of people in the combined groups. Then use the tables below to record the combined group survey results.

Total number of people in the combined groups: _____

What kind of store do you think is most important at a mall? (Choose only one.)	Number of people who chose that type of store (combined group totals)
A. clothing	
B. shoes	
C. CD/tape/video/ music	
D. sporting goods	
E. department store	
F. video arcade	

How often do you go to a mall?	Number of people who go that often (combined group totals)
A. one or more times a week	
B. once every 2 to 3 weeks	
C. once a month	
D. less than once a month	
E. never	

Name _____ Date _____

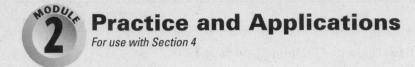

Practice and Applications
For use with Section 4

For use with Exploration 1

Tell whether each question is biased. Rewrite each biased question so that it is no longer biased.

1. Would not football be a better sport for you to play than field hockey?

2. Should students be allowed to eat their lunches outside the building in the courtyard?

3. Do you really like action films rather than dramas?

4. What is your favorite radio station?

5. The top grossing films as of 1997 are listed in the table below. Can you conclude that viewers would rather see fantasy films than other types of films? Why or why not?

Movie	Year	World gross receipts
Jurassic Park	1993	$913,000,000
Independence Day	1996	$798,000,000
The Lion King	1994	$772,000,000
Star Wars	1977–1997	$740,000,000
E.T.: The Extra Terrestrial	1982	$701,000,000

6. Suppose you did a survey of 34 car owners and asked them to list their preference of color for a car. The results are shown in the table at the right. Can you conclude that most people prefer dark green cars? Explain your answer.

Color	Number	Percent
Dark green	10	29.4
White	8	23.5
Light brown	6	17.6
Medium red	5	14.7
Black	5	14.7

For use with Exploration 2

7. Suppose a middle school survey is taken to find out if students should be allowed to eat their lunch outside during good weather. The survey is given only to eighth graders.

   a. What is the population? What is the sample?

   b. Is this a representative sample? Why or why not?

(continued)

Math Thematics, Book 3
Teacher's Resource Book, Modules 1 and 2

Name _____   Date _____

Practice and Applications
For use with Section 4

8. Use the information shown in the graph. Find the percent of all music media represented by each type of media.

   a. music videos

   b. compact discs

   c. tapes

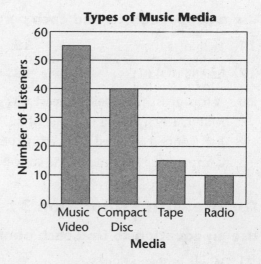

Estimate each percent. Tell which method you used.

9. 24% of 400

10. 56% of $200

11. 30% of 300

Marketing Use the information at the right for Exercises 12 and 13. Round decimal answers to the nearest unit.

In a survey of 800 teens:

56.2% listen to rock music radio stations

12% listen to new age music radio stations

33.8% listen to the radio at least once a day

12. **a.** Estimate how many of the teens listen to rock music radio stations. Then find the actual number.

   b. Estimate how many of the teens listen to new age music radio stations. Then find the actual number.

13. **a.** Estimate how many of the teens listen to the radio at least once a day.

   b. Use the "Undoing" method to find the actual number of teens who listen to the radio once a day.

   c. Use the "Equivalent Fraction" method to find the number of teens who listen to the radio once a day.

   d. Based on your answers to parts (b) and (c), which method do you prefer? Explain.

(continued)

Math Thematics, Book 3
Teacher's Resource Book, Modules 1 and 2   **2-49**

Name _____ Date _____

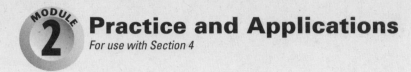

Practice and Applications

For use with Section 4

Use a proportion to find each percent.

14. 18% of 340

15. 175% of 92

16. 16.8% of 600

17. 62.4% of 430

18. 0.4% of 8000

19. 115% of 12

20. A top-grossing music concert was given by the Rolling Stones in March 1995, with a revenue of $27,600,000. If the Elton John/Billy Joel concert in April 1995 earned $4,400,000, use a percent to compare the revenue of the concerts.

For use with Exploration 3

Use an equation to find each number or percent.

21. What is 60% of 90?

22. 0.8% of 20 is what number?

23. 45 is what percent of 225?

24. 6 is what percent of 300?

25. 6.3 is 9% of what number?

26. 42 is 175% of what number?

27. 84 is what percent of 56?

28. 8% of what number is 24?

29. The average number of customers in a restaurant on a typical day in January is 28. To increase the number of customers the manager advertises that the second meal of equal or lesser cost will be free to the first 10 customers when the first meal is ordered. On the next night in January, the number of free meals served was 20% of the total number of customers.

    a. Write an equation and find the total number of meals ordered in the restaurant that day.

    b. Do you think the free meal giveaway helped increase the number of customers? Why or why not?

    c. Suppose the free meals averaged $15, and the price of a regular meal averages $21. Was the promotion a good idea? Explain your answer.

Name _____ Date _____

Study Guide
For use with Section 4

2-51

Your Opinion Counts! Surveys, Proportions, and Percents

GOAL **LEARN HOW TO:** • use percents, fractions, and decimals to summarize
the results of a survey
• identify and correct biased survey questions
• use proportional reasoning to estimate the percent of a number
• identify representative samples
• write equations to solve percent problems
• find a representative sample

AS YOU: • conduct a survey
• make predictions based on a sample
• analyze the results of the Mall Survey

Exploration 1: Conducting a Survey

You can conduct a survey to get information about people's opinions.
When a question produces responses that do not accurately reflect the
opinions of the people surveyed, it is a **biased question**. A survey should
contain no biased questions.

Exploration 2: Proportions and Percents

Surveys

A survey is used to gather information about a group called a
population. When it is not practical to contact every member
of the population, a smaller group called a **sample** is surveyed.
The survey results are used to make predictions about the whole
population.

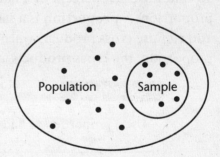

Representative Samples

Care must be taken when choosing a sample. To make accurate
predictions based on a sample, the sample must be a *representative
sample* of the total population. A **representative sample** has the
same characteristics as the population being studied.

Study Guide
For use with Section 4

Estimating Percents

You can use a "nice" fraction to estimate the percent of a number, or you can use multiples of 10%.

Example

Estimate 27% of 600.

▪ Sample Response ▪

27% is close to both 25% and 30%.

Using 25%:

25% equals the "nice" fraction $\frac{1}{4}$.

$\frac{1}{4}$ of 600 = $\frac{1}{4}$ • 600 = 150

Using 30%:

10% of 600 is 60, so 30% of 600 is 3 • 60 = 180.

Since 25% < 27% < 30%, 27% of 600 is between 150 and 180.

Finding Percents

To find the exact percent of a number, you can write and solve a proportion. A **proportion** is a statement that two ratios are equal. You can use cross products when solving a proportion. In a proportion, the **cross products** are equal.

Example

Use a proportion to find 27% of 600.

▪ Sample Response ▪

$$\begin{array}{cc} & \text{Percent} \quad \text{Number} \end{array}$$

$$\begin{array}{l} \text{part} \rightarrow \\ \text{whole} \rightarrow \end{array} \frac{27}{100} = \frac{x}{600} \begin{array}{l} \leftarrow \text{part} \\ \leftarrow \text{whole} \end{array}$$

$$27 • 600 = 100 • x \quad \leftarrow \text{The cross products are equal.}$$

$$16{,}200 = 100x \quad \leftarrow \text{Divide both sides by 100.}$$

$$162 = x$$

So, 27% of 600 is 162.

Name _____   Date _____

Study Guide
For use with Section 4

Exploration 3: Samples and Percents

Finding Parts, Percents, and Totals

You can find an exact percent of a number by writing and solving
an equation. You can also use equations to find what percent one
number is of another number or to find a total when you know a part
and the corresponding percent.

Example

Write and solve an equation to find each number or percent.

a. What is 27% of 600?

b. 12 is what percent of 240?

c. 65 is 50% of what number?

Sample Response

a. Think: 27% of 600 is what number?

Now write this sentence as an equation and solve the equation.

$0.27 \cdot 600 = x$ ← Write 27% as a decimal.

$162 = x$

So, 27% of 600 is 162.

b. $12 = \frac{x}{100} \cdot 240$ ← Write the missing percent as a fraction.

$12 = \frac{240}{100}x$

$12 = 2.4x$

$5 = x$

So, 12 is 5% of 240.

c. $65 = 0.50 \cdot x$ ← Write the percent as a decimal.

$65 = 0.5x$

$130 = x$

So, 65 is 50% of 130.

Study Guide: Practice & Application Exercises

For use with Section 4

Exploration 1

Tell whether each question is biased. Rewrite each biased question so that it is no longer biased.

1. Wouldn't Kelly make a better class president than Rachel?

2. Should students use pen, which is hard to erase, or pencil to do math?

3. Which type of book do you like better, fiction or nonfiction?

Exploration 2

4. Suppose a manufacturer of baby food is conducting a survey to find the ages of babies who are most likely to eat their applesauce. The survey is sent to every household that mailed in the company's rebate offer during the previous year.

   a. What is the population? What is the sample?

   b. Is this a representative sample? Explain.

Estimate each percent. Tell which method you used.

5. 73% of 400   6. 39% of 250   7. 21% of $37

8. 32% of 9000   9. 59% of $350   10. 87% of 480

Use a proportion to find each percent.

11. 300% of 72   12. 35% of 112   13. 15% of 74

14. 24% of 350   15. 0.1% of 45,000   16. 43.8% of 1000

Exploration 3

Use an equation to find each number or percent.

17. What is 20% of 38?   18. 16% of what number is 8?

19. 54 is what percent of 15?   20. What is 27% of 350?

21. 150% of what number is 540?   22. 117 is what percent of 234?

23. On a recent Spanish quiz, 15 students got an A. If 75% of the class got an A, how many students are in the class?

24. Last week, 78 students attended a football game. To increase attendance, the football team held a pep rally before this week's game. This week's attendance was 150% of last week's attendance. How many more students attended this week's game?

Name _____   Date _____

Quick Quiz
For use after Section 4

1. Jayne Middle School is conducting a survey to decide whether 7th and 8th graders should be allowed to eat lunch outside. Tell whether each group would be a representative sample. Explain your thinking.

   a. all students in the 7th and 8th grades with birthdays before June 30

   b. the students in Ms. Jones's seventh-grade science class

2. Tell whether the question is biased. If it is, rewrite it so that it is no longer biased.

   "Should athletes spend less of their valuable time practicing sports and more time studying?"

3. Estimate 74% of 400. Tell what method you used.

4. Use a proportion to find 34% of 350.

Use an equation to find each number or percent.

5. What is 48% of 120?

6. 24% of what number is 33?

7. 12 is what percent of 96?

Name _____   Date _____

Warm-Up Exercises
For use with Section 5

Use mental math to find each answer.

1. 10% of 60

2. 20% of 60

3. 5% of 60

4. 25% of 60

5. 15% of 60

6. 95% of 60

ANSWERS

1. 6   2. 12   3. 3   4. 15   5. 9   6. 57

Name _____   Date _____

Bargain Basement Game Cards (Use with Question 5 on page 141.)

Directions Cut out the cards and use them to play *Bargain Basement.*

Cordless Phone		Tape Player	
Store A	10% off $50	Store A	10% off $80
Store B	$\frac{1}{2}$ off $90	Store B	$\frac{1}{4}$ off $90
Store C	55% off $100	Store C	30% off $100
Store D	$33\frac{1}{3}$% off $60	Store D	5% off $69.95

Jeans		35 mm Camera	
Store A	20% off $20	Store A	20% off $55
Store B	$\frac{1}{3}$ off $30	Store B	$\frac{1}{2}$ off $94.95
Store C	25% off $32	Store C	$15 off $58
Store D	40% off $50	Store D	60% off $120

Sunglasses		Compact Disc	
Store A	50% off $19.95	Store A	20% off $14.95
Store B	$\frac{1}{3}$ off $15	Store B	$\frac{1}{5}$ off $15
Store C	20% off $11	Store C	40% off $20
Store D	10% off $10	Store D	7% off $21.88

Graphing Calculator		Roller Blades	
Store A	25% off $80	Store A	15% off $100
Store B	$\frac{1}{4}$ off $88	Store B	$\frac{1}{3}$ off $119.95
Store C	15% off $70	Store C	25% off $120
Store D	50% off $120	Store D	60% off $190

Air Mattress		Bike Helmet	
Store A	10% off $15	Store A	85% off $80
Store B	60% off $40	Store B	$\frac{3}{5}$ off $45
Store C	$10 off $24.95	Store C	60% off $50
Store D	20% off $25	Store D	12% off $29.95

Name _____ Date _____

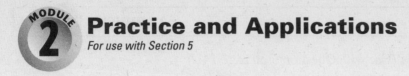

MODULE 2 Practice and Applications
For use with Section 5

For use with Exploration 1

1. Find 51% of $39.99. Describe two different ways to find the number.

For Exercises 2–7, estimate the answer. Then find the exact answer.

2. 33% of 120   **3.** 60% of 48

4. 9% of 700   **5.** 41% of 250

6. 19% of 230   **7.** 49% of 200

A store advertises that all prices are 25–50 percent off. The price tags below represent the tags used by a store to label its sale prices. The original price is crossed out on each sale tag, and the sale price is written above. Use estimation or mental math to check that each price is within the advertised range. Tell which tags are marked incorrectly and explain how you know.

8.

$26.00
$49.95

9.
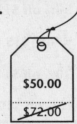
$50.00
$72.00

10.

$60.00
$79.95

11.

$64.00
$120.00

12.

$62.00
$89.95

13.

$2.50
$10.95

(continued)

Math Thematics, Book 3
Teacher's Resource Book, Modules 1 and 2

Name _____ Date _____

Practice and Applications
For use with Section 5

For use with Exploration 2

14. Suppose a store's sales increased 8% from June to July and 8% from July to August.

   a. Sales were $8199 in June. Estimate the sales in July.

   b. Use your estimate in part (a) to estimate the sales in August.

   c. Find the actual sales in July. Then use your answer to find the actual sales in August. Compare the answers with your estimates.

   d. Harry thinks that since sales increased 8% in July and 8% in August, they increased by the same number of dollars each month. Is he correct? Explain why or why not.

15. In 1992, a typical starting salary for a college graduate with a degree in computer science was $30,890. In 1993, the typical starting salary was $31,600.

   a. Estimate the percent of change in starting salary from 1992 to 1993. Explain your method of estimating.

   b. Find the actual percent of change in starting salary from 1992 to 1993. How does it compare with your estimate?

16. In 1979, there were 90 million workers in the United States. In 1992, there were 108 million workers.

   a. Estimate the percent of change in the number of workers from 1979 to 1992. Explain your method of estimating.

   b. Find the actual percent of change in the number of workers from 1979 to 1992. How does it compare with your estimate?

17. The number of cars and light trucks sold in the United States is shown in the graph.

   a. Find the percent of increase from 1991 to 1993.

   b. Find the percent of decrease from 1990 to 1991.

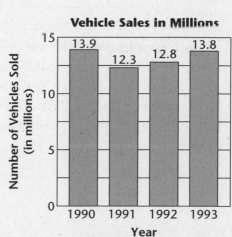

Study Guide
For use with Section 5

The Price is Right, Isn't It?   Working with Percents

GOAL **LEARN HOW TO:** • estimate percents
                              • use mental math to find percents
                              • use percents to solve problems
                              • estimate percents of change

AS YOU: • play *Bargain Basement*
            • analyze sale prices

Exploration 1: Estimating with Percents

Estimating Percents

You can use estimation or mental math to find a percent of a number.

Example

Find the amount of the discount and the sale price of a $28 watch on sale for 25% off.

Sample Response

First, find the amount of the discount.

Method 1: Use a decimal.

25% = 0.25
So, 25% of $28 is 0.25 • $28, or $7.

Method 2: Use a fraction.

$25\% = \frac{1}{4}$
So, 25% of $28 is $\frac{1}{4}$ • $28, or $7.

Now, find the sale price.

The sale price of an item is found by subtracting the amount of the discount from the original price.

So, the sale price of the watch is $28 − $7, or $21.

In the Example above, the sale price could have been found another way. Since the watch is being sold for 25% off the original price, this means you must pay 100% − 25%, or 75% of the original price. So the sale price can be obtained by finding 75% of $28, or 0.75 • $28 = $21. The amount of the discount can then be found by subtracting the sale price from the original price: $28 − $21 = $7.

Math Thematics, Book 3
2-60 Teacher's Resource Book, Modules 1 and 2

Name _____   Date _____

Study Guide

For use with Section 5

Exploration 2: Percent of Change

A percent discount is an example of a **percent of decrease**. You can find a percent of decrease by using a ratio.

$$\text{Percent of decrease} = \frac{\text{amount of decrease}}{\text{original amount}}$$

Example

What percent of decrease do you receive when you pay $40 for a $50 sweater?

■ Sample Response ■

To use the percent of decrease ratio, you need to find the amount of decrease and you need to identify the original amount.

The original price is $50. The decrease in price is $50 − $40, or $10.

$$\text{Percent of decrease} = \frac{\text{amount of decrease}}{\text{original amount}}$$
$$= \frac{\$10}{\$50} = 0.2, \text{ or } 20\%$$

So, there is a 20% discount on the sweater.

A **percent of increase** is also an example of a **percent of change**. A percent of increase can be used to describe price markups and other increases.

$$\text{Percent of increase} = \frac{\text{amount of increase}}{\text{original amount}}$$

Example

A discount store paid $15 for each copy of a software program. If the store is selling the program for $20, what is the percent of increase?

■ Sample Response ■

To use the percent of increase ratio, you need to find the amount of increase and you need to identify the original amount.

The original amount is $15. The increase in price (*markup*) is $20 − $15, or $5.

$$\text{Percent of increase} = \frac{\text{amount of increase}}{\text{original amount}}$$
$$= \frac{\$5}{\$15} = 0.333..., \text{ or } 33\tfrac{1}{3}\%$$

So, there was a $33\tfrac{1}{3}\%$ markup on the computer program.

Study Guide: Practice & Application Exercises
For use with Section 5

Exploration 1

1. Describe two different ways to estimate 73% of $149.95.

For Exercises 2–9, estimate the answer. Then find the exact answer.

2. 49% of 36 **3.** 19% of 300 **4.** 60% of 13 **5.** 4% of 122

6. 23% of 64 **7.** 15% of 78 **8.** 89% of 205 **9.** 11% of 112

10. Find the amount of the discount and the sale price of a $30 pair of jeans on sale for 20% off.

11. Find the amount of the discount and the sale price of a $75 jacket on sale for 30% off.

12. Find the amount of the discount and the sale price of a $15 book on sale for 40% off.

Exploration 2

13. What percent of decrease do you get if you pay $29.25 for a $65 pair of pants?

14. What is the percent of increase on a paperback book selling for $5 that cost the bookstore $2?

15. What is the percent of increase on a box of cereal selling for $4.50 that cost the grocery store $1.50?

16. What percent of decrease do you get if you pay $18 for a 15 lb ham that normally sells for $32?

Use the table for Exercises 17–19.

17. Find the percent of increase in the average score from November to January.

18. Find the percent of decrease in the average score from January to February.

19. Find the percent of change in the average score from September to June.

Average Scores on a Science Test	
Month	**Score**
September	76
October	81
November	74
December	85
January	89
February	82
March	93
April	90
May	95
June	91

Name _____   Date _____

Quick Quiz

For use after Section 5

1. Estimate 70% of 88. Then find the exact answer.

2. A clothing store advertises that sweaters are 40–50% off. If a sweater that was originally priced at $39.95 is now $25.95, is the store advertisement correct? Explain.

3. In 1975, there were 9000 youth softball teams. In 1990 there were 46,000 and in 1999 there were 83,000.

   a. Find the percent of change from 1975 to 1990. Round to the nearest percent.

   b. Find the percent of change from 1990 to 1999. Round to the nearest percent.

   c. Use percent of change to write a short summary about how the number of youth softball teams changed from 1975 to 1999.

Name _____ Date _____

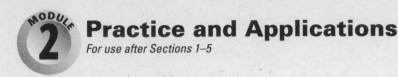

Practice and Applications
For use after Sections 1–5

For use with Section 1

For Exercises 1–4, simplify each expression.

1. $35 + (-23)$ **2.** $-5 \cdot (-19)$ **3.** $88 \div (-11)$ **4.** $-9 - 25$

Solve each equation.

5. $|x| = 5$ **6.** $|y| = 12$ **7.** $-t = 22$ **8.** $-m = -3$

Use the figure shown.

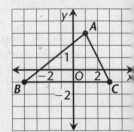

9. a. Give the coordinates of points A, B, and C.

     b. Give the coordinates of the image points A', B', and C' after a translation of $(x - 1, y + 2)$.

For use with Section 2

Find each sum or difference.

10. $-\dfrac{2}{3} + \left(-\dfrac{2}{3}\right)$ **11.** $\dfrac{5}{6} - \left(-\dfrac{7}{20}\right)$ **12.** $-5\dfrac{1}{4} - \dfrac{3}{8}$

13. $-3\dfrac{1}{5} + 2\dfrac{2}{5}$ **14.** $-1\dfrac{1}{2} - \left(-2\dfrac{1}{8}\right)$ **15.** $4\dfrac{5}{7} + \left(-3\dfrac{2}{9}\right)$

For use with Section 3

A box contains 3 red pens, 5 blue pens, and a green pen. Find the theoretical probability of each event.

16. pulling out a red pen on the first try

17. not pulling out a green pen on the first try

18. pulling out a blue pen after two red pens have been removed

19. A bus driver is asked to choose the order in which she will pick up three students: Agnes, Bill, and Clara.

     a. Draw a tree diagram to show all the possible orders in which the students could be picked up.

     b. Find the probability that the bus driver will choose an order in which Clara will be picked up before Bill.

(continued)

Math Thematics, Book 3
2-64   Teacher's Resource Book, Modules 1 and 2

Name _____   Date _____

Practice and Applications
For use after Sections 1–5

For use with Section 4

Use a proportion to find each percent.

20. 19% of 340   **21.** 1% of 675   **22.** 51% of 30

23. 100% of 45   **24.** 2.5% of 1200   **25.** 24% of 365

Estimate each percent.

26. 12% of 500   **27.** 24% of 6000   **28.** 99% of 354

Use an equation to find each percent or number.

29. 49 is what percent of 52?   **30.** What is 26% of 20?

A survey is given to find out how the summer programs sponsored by the Youth Group are rated. The survey is given to parents of the children who attended last year.

31. What is the population? What is the sample?

32. Is this a representative sample? Why or why not?

For use with Section 5

Use the table for Exercises 33 and 34.

33. Estimate the percent of change in newspaper sales from June to July.

34. Estimate the percent of change in the cost of a newspaper from June to July.

Newspaper Sales (in dollars)		
Month	Total sales	Price per paper
June	$530	$1.00
July	$450	$1.25

Find each percent of change.

35. A $23.00 book sells for $13.80.

36. A child grows from 150 cm tall to 162 cm tall.

Name _____   Date _____

Inventory List (Use with the Module Project on pages 150–151.)

Directions The items for sale in your game, along with their least and greatest possible prices, are given below. You must use these items and the price information in your game in some way.

Item	Maximum price	Minimum sale price
digital watch	$29.99	$17.50
jeans	$35.00	$17.00
basketball	$12.99	$10.00
backpack	$35.00	$19.00
sandals	$17.99	$12.00
athletic shoes	$45.00	$25.00
CD	$17.99	$10.00
T-shirt	$22.99	$7.99
movie video	$29.99	$18.00
fanny pack	$15.99	$9.00
CD player	$135.00	$69.99
purse	$24.99	$15.00
athletic socks	$2.99	$0.99
computer game	$69.99	$40.00

Name _____   Date _____

Game Board (Use with the Module Project on pages 150–151.)

Directions Use the game board to make a game that imitates shopping at a mall.

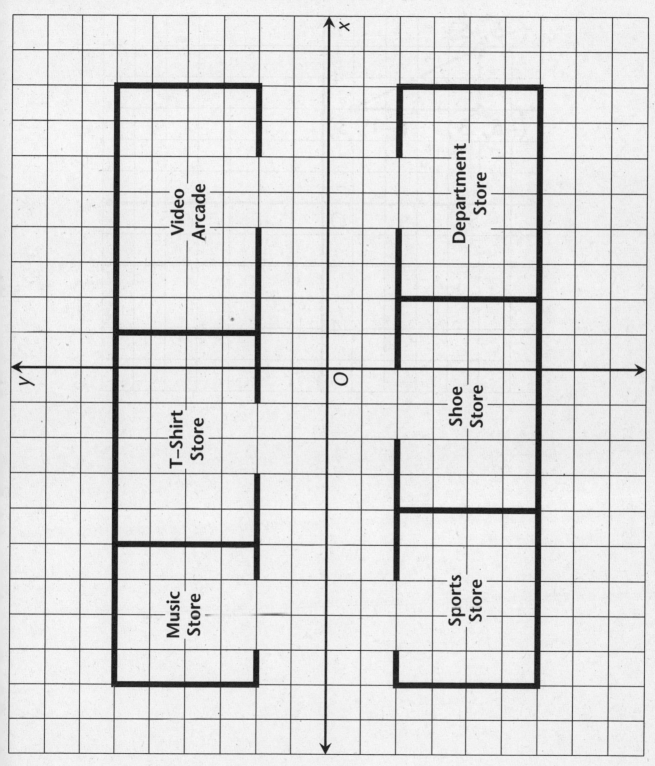

MODULE 2   **REVIEW AND ASSESSMENT LABSHEET**

Cyber Spaceship Obstacle (Use with Exercise 14 on page 152.)

Directions Draw the image of the triangle after the translation $(x + 6, y + (-4))$.

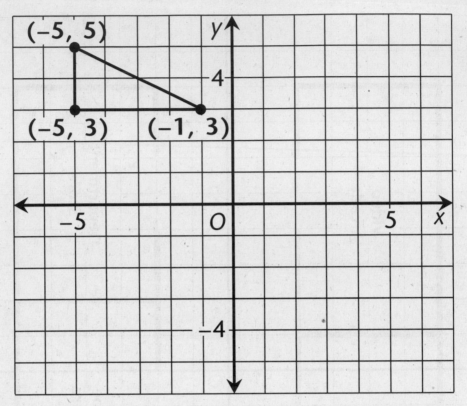

Name _____ Date _____

Test Form A
For use after Module 2

Evaluate each expression.

1. $102 \div (-42)$

2. $6 - (-8)$

3. $-4 - 14$

4. $-8 \cdot 12$

5. $(-17)(-3)$

6. $-16 \div (-8)$

7. $3(-4)(-7) \div (-6)$

8. $-40 + 8 - (-11)$

9. What two numbers have an absolute value of 7?

10. What is the opposite of -12? Explain how you know it is the opposite.

11. The coordinates of the vertices of a triangle are: $Q(3, 5)$, $R(0, -7)$, and $S(-5, 8)$. The coordinates of the vertices of the image of the triangle after a translation are: $Q'(6, -1)$, $R'(3, -13)$, and $S'(-2, 2)$. Write two expressions that describe the translation.

Find each sum or difference. Write your answers in lowest terms.

12. $-\dfrac{3}{4} + \dfrac{5}{8}$

13. $-\dfrac{4}{7} - \dfrac{3}{5}$

14. $-3\dfrac{1}{4} + 2\dfrac{3}{8}$

15. $-1\dfrac{7}{10} + \left(-4\dfrac{3}{5}\right)$

For Questions 16–18, suppose a bag contains 1 red, 1 green, and 2 blue marbles. You are to draw 2 marbles from the bag one at a time without putting the first marble drawn back into the bag.

16. Draw a tree diagram to show all the possible outcomes.

17. What is the theoretical probability of picking 2 blue marbles?

18. Suppose you conduct an experiment to determine the color of the first marble taken from the bag. In each trial, you take a marble from the bag, record the color, then replace it. The results are shown in the table. What is the experimental probability of drawing a blue marble?

50 trials		
Red	**Green**	**Blue**
18	12	20

Test Form A

For use after Module 2

19. Is the following survey question biased? If so, rewrite the question so that it is no longer biased.

"Do you think bicycle helmets should be required for all cyclists?"

20. The Coffeemaker is conducting a survey to decide whether to open a coffee stand on Main Street from 8 A.M. to 10 A.M. each day. Describe a group that would be a representative sample.

21. In a survey of boys and girls 12–14 years old, 74% of the girls and 52% of the boys said situation comedies ("sitcoms") were their favorite type of TV program. Suppose 850 girls were surveyed. How many of the girls said sitcoms were their favorite type of TV show?

For Questions 22 and 23, estimate each answer. Describe the strategy you used.

22. An electronics store buys a computer for $750 and marks up the price to $1100 for resale. Estimate the percent of markup.

23. A $98 CD player is discounted 40%. Estimate the sale price.

24. The table shows the number of overnight stays in U.S. National Parks. Find the percent of change from 1990 to 1999 for each type of lodging. Round to the nearest whole percent.

National Park Overnight Stays (in millions)		
	1990	1999
Commercial lodgings	3.9	3.7
Park Service campgrounds	7.9	6.2
In back country	1.7	2.0

Name _____ Date _____

Test Form B
For use after Module 2

2-71

Evaluate each expression.

1. $92 + (-31)$

2. $8 - (-9)$

3. $-3 - 11$

4. $-6 \cdot 14$

5. $(-16)(-4)$

6. $-15 \div (-3)$

7. $6(-3)(-5) \div (-10)$

8. $-32 + 9 - (-13)$

9. What two numbers have an absolute value of 9?

10. What is the opposite of -15? Explain how you know it is the opposite.

11. The coordinates of the vertices of a triangle are: $Q(3, 5)$, $R(0, -7)$, and $S(-5, 8)$. The coordinates of the vertices of the image of the triangle after a translation are: $Q'(1, 9)$, $R'(-2, -3)$, and $S'(-7, 12)$. Write two expressions that describe the translation.

Find each sum or difference. Write your answers in lowest terms.

12. $-\dfrac{4}{7} + \dfrac{2}{3}$

13. $-\dfrac{5}{8} - \left(-\dfrac{3}{5}\right)$

14. $-2\dfrac{1}{3} + 1\dfrac{1}{2}$

15. $-2\dfrac{3}{10} + \left(-3\dfrac{4}{5}\right)$

For Questions 16–18, suppose a bag contains 2 red, 1 green, and 2 yellow marbles. You are to draw 2 marbles from the bag one at a time without putting the first marble drawn back into the bag.

16. Draw a tree diagram to show all the possible outcomes.

17. What is the theoretical probability of picking 2 red marbles?

18. Suppose you conduct an experiment to determine the color of the first marble taken from the bag. In each trial, you take a marble from the bag, record the color, then replace it. The results are shown in the table. What is the experimental probability of drawing a yellow marble?

50 trials		
Red	Green	Yellow
24	11	17

Test Form B
For use after Module 2

19. Is the following survey question biased? If so, rewrite the question so that it is no longer biased.

"Do you think people diet too much?"

20. Mountain School is conducting a survey of students to decide whether its school year should include winter vacation so that winter sports could be enjoyed. Describe a group that would be a representative sample.

21. In a survey of boys and girls 12–14 years old, 42% of the girls and 78% of the boys said that science fiction movies were their favorite type of movie rental. Suppose 1320 boys answered that science fiction movies were their favorite type of movie rental. How many boys were surveyed?

For Questions 22 and 23, estimate each answer. Describe the strategy you used.

22. A music store buys a compact disc for $6.50 and marks up the price to $14.95 for resale. Estimate the percent of markup.

23. A $78.50 item is discounted 30%. Estimate the sale price.

24. The table shows the spending on entertainment media in 2005, and the projected spending in 2009. Find the predicted change in each category from 2005 to 2009. Round your answers to the nearest whole percent.

Spending on Entertainment Media (in billions of dollars)		
	2005	2009
DVDs	$26.7	$40.4
Videocassettes	$4.1	$1.6
Videogames	$9.6	$15.1

Name _____   Date _____

Standardized Test
For use after Module 2

1. Of 8400 adults who registered complaints with the Better Business Bureau, 10.3% complained about auto repair and service. How many complaints were made about auto repair and service?
  a. 800   **b.** 840
  c. 865   **d.** 8652

2. Of 8400 adults who registered complaints with the Better Business Bureau, 2325 complaints were about retail sales. What percent is this?
  a. 27%   **b.** 28%
  c. 56%   **d.** 361%

3. A grocery store buys a pound of meat for $1.40 and marks up the price to $2.50. Find the percent of markup.
  a. 27%   **b.** 44%
  c. 56%   **d.** 79%

4. A $49.50 item is discounted 40%. Estimate the sale price.
  a. $3   **b.** $20
  c. $30   **d.** $70

5. Simplify $-4\frac{2}{5} - 2\frac{3}{4}$.
  a. $-1\frac{13}{20}$ **b.** $-6\frac{3}{4}$
  c. $-7\frac{3}{20}$ **d.** $-\frac{130}{5}$

6. What is the value of $-9 + 14 - (-5)$?
  a. -18   **b.** -10
  c. 0   **d.** 10

7. What is the experimental probability of picking three greens in a row?
  a. $\frac{1}{32}$
  b. $\frac{1}{4}$
  c. $\frac{4}{8}$
  d. $\frac{7}{10}$

	1st Pick	2nd Pick	3rd Pick
	Green	Green — Green / Red — Green	
	Blue	Green — Green / Red — Green	

8. Suppose two marbles are drawn from a box containing 2 yellow, 2 blue, and 1 green marble. What is the theoretical probability that both marbles are yellow?
  a. $\frac{2}{5}$ **b.** $\frac{2}{3}$
  c. $\frac{1}{10}$ **d.** $\frac{1}{5}$

9. Which of the following is not biased?
  a. Do you really like that TV program?
  b. How many unhealthy snacks did you eat today?
  c. What is your favorite Internet site?
  d. Did you get enough exercise today?

10. Find the coordinates of the point $(-4, 5)$ after the translation $(x + 4, y - 3)$.
  a. $(0, 2)$ **b.** $(-16, -15)$
  c. $(-8, -8)$ **d.** $(0, 9)$

11. Simplify $\frac{3}{8} - \left(-\frac{3}{5}\right)$.
  a. 2   **b.** $\frac{39}{40}$
  c. $\frac{6}{13}$ **d.** $-\frac{9}{40}$

12. What is the value of $12(-4)(-6) \div (-3)$?
  a. -96   **b.** -18
  c. 18   **d.** 96

Name _____   Date _____

Module Performance Assessment
For use after Module 2

Vickie wanted to create a game for a school project. First she made a spinner like the one shown at the right. In her game, on each turn, the player spins the spinner twice.

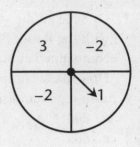

1. Draw a tree diagram of all possible outcomes of the two spins.

2. What is the probability the player will get –2 on both spins?

3. What is the probability the player will get –2 on the first spin and 3 on the second spin?

4. In Vickie's game, the numbers a player spins are multiplied together. Create a line plot showing all the possible products.

5. What percent of the products are greater than 0?

6. What percent of the products are greater than or equal to –2?

7. Suppose a player took 12 turns (each turn is 2 spins of the spinner). About how many products of –6 would you expect the player to get?

8. Vickie decided that after 16 turns the players will add all of their products. The player with the sum closest to 0 wins. Do you think this is a fair game? Explain.

Name _____   Date _____

Cumulative Test
For use after Modules 1 and 2

For Questions 1 and 2, use the stem-and-leaf plot of high temperatures on Dec. 19, 1997, in 24 cities.

High Temperatures Dec. 19

```
3 | 4 6 6 9
4 | 0 1 1 3 3 4 4 4 5 5 5 6 8 9 9
5 | 3 6 7 9 9
```

4 | 1 means 41° F

1. **a.** Find the mean, median, and mode of the data set.

   b. Which average from part (a) do you think best represents the data set? Explain your thinking.

2. **a.** Construct a box-and-whisker plot for the data.

   b. Give the range, lower extreme, upper extreme, lower quartile, and upper quartile.

   c. What percent of the data is represented by the box from the box-and-whisker plot?

3. The table shows the distance and time for a trip.

   a. Construct a scatter plot of the data. Put time on the horizontal axis.

   b. Is there a positive correlation, a negative correlation, or no correlation between the time and the distance?

   c. Use a straight line or a smooth curve to connect the points.

   d. Use your graph to predict how long it will take to travel 400 mi.

Distance (mi)	Time (hr)
0	0
50	1
120	2
175	3
220	4
275	5

The circle graph shows the percentage of science classes offered at a high school.

Science Classes

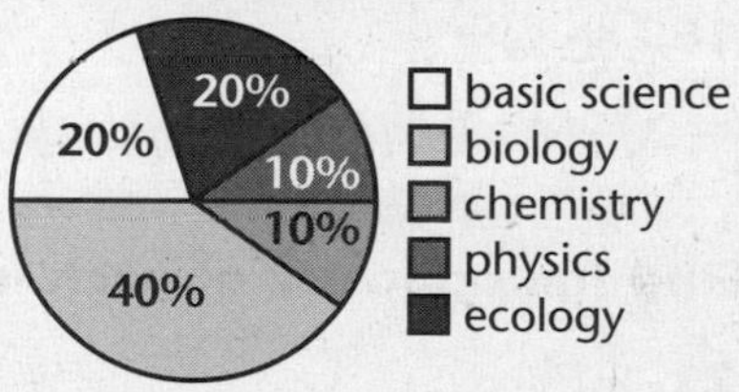

20% — basic science
20% — biology
10% — chemistry
10% — physics
40% — ecology

4. What percent of science classes are biology?

5. If there are a total of 30 classes offered, how many are basic science or ecology?

6. Without measuring, give the angle measure of the sector for physics.

7. The number of stations in the longest underground rail networks in the world are given. Draw a histogram of the number of stations using intervals of 100.

   270, 469, 432, 250, 150, 154, 145, 70, 135, 130

Name _____   Date _____

Cumulative Test
For use after Modules 1 and 2

Solve each equation.

8. $18 = 4y - 6$

9. $\frac{z}{4} + 2 = 10$

10. $|x| = 6$

11. Simplify $3f^2 + 3f - 2f^2 - 2f + 3$.

12. Of 325 eighth-graders who voted for a class president, 48% were female. How many females voted?

13. A motorcycle shop buys a new motorcycle for $1050 and sells it for $2000. What is the percent of increase after the markup?

14. A gumball machine in a grocery store has only 2 red gumballs, 2 green ones, and 1 yellow gumball left. You can buy two gumballs.

    a. Draw a tree diagram to show all the possible outcomes.

    b. What is the theoretical probability of getting 2 green gumballs?

Evaluate each expression.

15. $-14 + 8$

16. $-32 - 9$

17. $-12 - (-6)$

18. $8(-7)$

19. $\frac{-84}{-7}$

20. $-2(-6)(-9)$

Find the opposite of each integer.

21. -14

22. 0

23. Draw the triangle after the translation $(x + 3, y + 2)$.

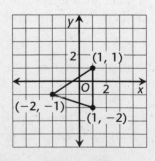

Find each sum or difference.

24. $-\frac{2}{3} + \frac{5}{6}$

25. $-\frac{1}{5} - \frac{3}{4}$

26. $-3\frac{3}{4} - \left(-4\frac{2}{3}\right)$

Math Thematics, Book 3
CT-2   Teacher's Resource Book, Modules 1 and 2

Answer Key

For use before Module 1

Book 3 Pre-Course Test (p. TR-32)

1. $=$
2. $<$
3. $>$
4. 225.9
5. 9.18
6. 0.00528
7. 56.05
8. 48.75
9. 9.8
10. Yes.
11. Yes.
12. No.
13. 9; 90
14. 1; 850
15. 15; 3600
16. 10
17. 35
18. 3
19. $\frac{21}{40}$
20. $\frac{11}{56}$
21. $\frac{4}{5}$
22. $\frac{1}{8}$
23. $\frac{5}{2}$ or $2\frac{1}{2}$
24. $\frac{5}{8}$
25. 0.12; 12%
26. 0.9; 90%
27. 0.85; 85%
28. 15
29. 18
30. 50
31. $-2, 1, 2$
32. $-5, 0, 3, 6$
33. $-5, -3, 3, 4$
34. $(-4, 1)$
35. $(0, 2)$
36. $(4, -4)$
37. $(-2, -3)$
38. **a.** right **b.** scalene
39. **a.** obtuse **b.** isosceles
40. **a.** acute **b.** equilateral
41. The figure is a polygon because it is a plane figure that is closed and that is formed by (three) segments that do not cross each other. It is a regular polygon because all the angles are of equal measure and all the sides are of equal length.
42. 84 m^3
43. 160 cm^3
44. mean: 16; median: 18; modes: 18 and 20; range: 13
45. mean: 55; median: 57; mode: none; range: 14

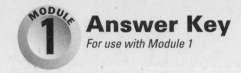

MODULE 1

Answer Key

For use with Module 1

MODULE 1

Diagnostic Test (p. 1-2)

1. **a.** equivalent
   b. not equivalent
2. **a.** 50%
   b. 25% of 32 = 8 classes
   c. 15% of 360 = 54°

3.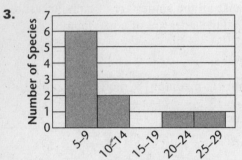

4. **a.** Percentile Scores

Class A	5	Class B
0	5	2 7 8
9	1 6	8 8
6 6 6 3	7	4 6
8 8 7 3 3	8	1 5
8 7 7	9	0 4 6

6 | 7 | means 76 | 7 | 4 means 74

   b. Class A: mean ≈ 80.13, median = 83,
   mode = 76
   Class B: mean ≈ 74.92, median = 75,
   mode = 68

5. **a.** Class B; the upper and lower extremes
   match the data.
   b.
   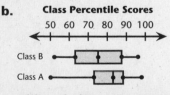

   c. Although the range, upper extremes,
   and upper quartiles for the two classes are
   about the same, Class A did significantly
   better than Class B. In fact, almost 75% of
   Class A scored higher than the lower 50%
   of Class B.

6. **a.** $x = 98$
   b. $y = 9$
   c. $m = 6$
7. **a.** $10x + 8$
   b. $17x^2 + 6x$
   c. no like terms
8. **a. and c.**
   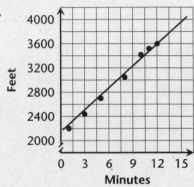

   b. positive correlation
   d. about 3950 ft
9. 9 and 4
10. 192 cm

SECTION 1

Practice and Applications (p. 1-11)

1. **a.** miles per hour; 52 mi/hr
   b. cost in dollars per pound; $2.81/lb
   c. miles per gallon; about 18.22 mi/gal
   d. chirps per minute; 29 chirps/min
2. **a.** 90 **b.** $0.12 **c.** $355.77 **d.** 6
3. 8.75 mi/min
4. **a.** 42.7 mi/hr **b.** 384 mi **c.** 0.71 mi/min
   d. about 1.4 minutes
5. **a.** Sample Response: The Walker family
   drove at a rate of 70 mi/hr for 3.5 hr. How
   many miles did they travel?; 245 mi
   b. Sample Response: The Ryders' car
   averages 21 mi/gal. About how many miles
   could they expect to travel on 6.2 gal of
   gas?; 130.2 mi **c.** Sample Response: Cheese
   costs $2.50 per lb. What is the total cost of
   4 pounds?; $10 **d.** Sample Response: Susan
   earns $5.25 per hour for 4 hours. How much
   did she earn?; $21

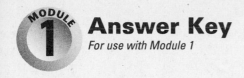

6. **a.** about 529.3 mi/hr **b.** about 8.82 mi/min
   c. about 10,585 mi

7. 17%

8. North America: 237.6°; Asia/Pacific Rim;
   50.4°; Europe: 61.2°; Other: 10.8°

9. 66,000,000

10.
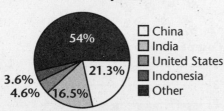

11. Sample Response:

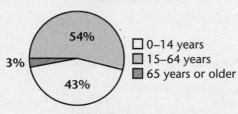

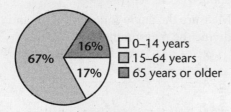

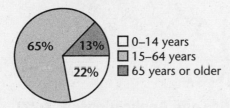

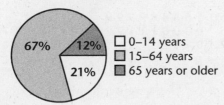

12. Sample Response: She was right because
    the data cannot be represented as percents.
    She could restructure the data so that she
    calculated the percent of each student that
    was between 4.5 ft and 5 ft, 5 ft and 5.5 ft,
    and so on as an example.

13. **a.** Sample Response:

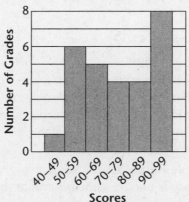

   b. Sample Response:

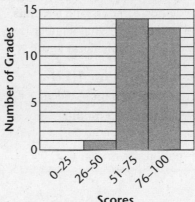

14. Sample Response:

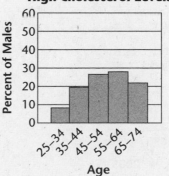

15.

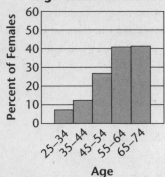

High Cholesterol Levels

(bar graph: Percent of Females vs Age: 25–34, 35–44, 45–54, 55–64, 65–74)

16. Sample Response: It seems that more women than men get high cholesterol as they get older. The percent of men is fairly stable as their age increases, but the percent of women increases.

17. No; Sample Response: Because the over 75 category is not the same interval as the others.

18. Sample Response: Probably not; because most people don't understand the units given and don't know what number is considered a high cholesterol figure.

Study Guide Exercises (p. 1-17)

1. pages per student; 6 pages/student

2. miles per minute; 0.75 mi/min

3. dollars per box; $5.27/box

4. miles per gallon; 32 mi/gal

5. $3.50

6. 60

7. $0.46

8. 24

9. 13%

10. 126°

11.

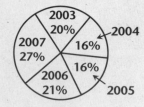

Truck Sales at Auto World

(circle graph: 2003 20%, 2004 16%, 2005 16%, 2006 21%, 2007 27%)

12.

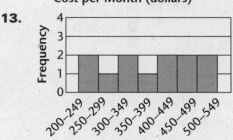

(histogram: Frequency vs Cost per Month (dollars): 200–299, 300–399, 400–499, 500–599)

13.

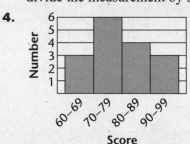

(histogram: Frequency vs Cost per Month (dollars): 200–249, 250–299, 300–349, 350–399, 400–449, 450–499, 500–549)

14. No, you do not have that information.

Quick Quiz (p. 1-18)

1. a. equivalent **b.** not equivalent

2. about 1.93 m/sec

3. Measure the angle for each sector and then divide the measurement by 360°.

4.

(histogram: Number vs Score: 60–69, 70–79, 80–89, 90–99)

SECTION 2

Practice and Applications (p. 1-22)

1. Heights of Eighth Grade Students

```
5 | 5 6 8 8 8 9 9 9 9
6 | 0 0 0 0 1 1 1 2 2 2 3 4 4 5 6 7 7 7 8 8
7 | 0 1 1 2 3
```

5 | 5 represents 55 in.

Answer Key

For use with Module 1

2. a. 18 in. **b.** mean: 63.1 in.; median: 62 in.; modes: 59 in., 60 in. **c.** Sample Response: The median because it is the middle of the height range.

3. a.

NBA Playoff Scores

Chicago Bulls		Utah Jazz
5	7	
9 4 0	8	4
8 8 6 5	9	2 3 6 8
9 7 0 0 0	10	0 1 3 4 4 5 6
	11	0

5 | 7 | represents 75 points. | 8 | 4 represents 84 points.

b. Sample Response: The scores for the Utah team were generally higher. **c.** range; Chicago: 34 points, Utah: 26 points; Sample Response: Chicago averages a wider spread or range in the points they score per game than Utah.

4. a. Chicago: mean, 94.7; median, 98; mode, 100; Utah: mean, 99.7; median, 101; mode, 104 **b.** mean; It may be the best average to predict future game scores.

5. Sample Response: because the previous scores did not reflect them playing each other

6. a. about 59% **b.** Sample Response: There are a larger number of students above the median height than below. **c.** about 50% **d.** They are the line segments showing the lower and upper extremes.

7. a. Chicago: 75; Utah: 84 **b.** Chicago: 109; Utah: 110 **c.** Chicago: 86.5; Utah: 94.5 **d.** Chicago: 100; Utah: 104.5

8. a. about 62% **b.** about 46%

9. a. Sample Response: The box-and-whisker plots on the same number line show that the median score for Utah is higher. **b.** both teams

10. Sample Response: Histogram; it shows the frequencies between intervals.

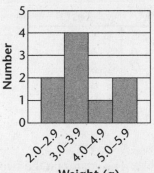

11. Sample Response: Scatter plot; it gives a visual picture of the varying lengths.

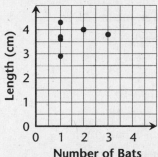

12. Sample Response: Scatter plot; it shows the relationship between 2 sets of data.

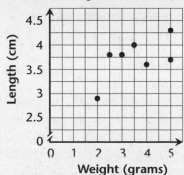

13. Sample Response: Box-and-whisker plot; it shows the median of 3.8.

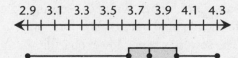

14. a–d. Answers may vary.

15. a–c. Answers may vary.

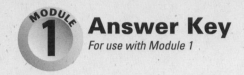

Answer Key

For use with Module 1

Study Guide Exercises (p. 1-28)

1.

Scores on Tests

Test A		Test B
0	5	5
8	6	5 6
6 5 5 2	7	5 5 8
8 6	8	5 8
6	9	8 9
0	10	

8 | 6 | represents a score of 68. | 7 | 5 represents a score of 75.

Sample Response: The scores on the two tests were about the same. Most scores were between 70 and 90.

2. Test A: mean: 78.6, median: 75.5, mode: 75; Test B: mean: 78.4, median: 76.5, mode: 75

3. males: 4; females: 8

4. males: 26; females: 22

5. males: 8; females: 10

6. males: 16; females: 18

7. Sample Response: bar graph

8. Sample Response: histogram

9. Sample Response: line graph

10. Sample Response: box-and-whisker plot

11. Sample Response: stem-and-leaf plot

12. Sample Response: scatter plot

Quick Quiz (p. 1-29)

1. a. Check students' work.
b. Class A: mean 78, median 79, mode 84; Class B: mean 81, median 85, mode 90

2. a. Class A; Sample Response: by the lower extreme **b.** Check students' plots: LE = 48, LQ = 75, Median = 85, UQ = 90, UE = 96
c. Sample Response: Only half of Class A scored 79 or higher, whereas 75% of Class B scored 75 or higher, with 50% scoring 85 or higher compared to only 25% for Class A.

3. a. The lower extreme, lower quartile, and median would all be 1, so the plot would not be very helpful for comparisons.
b. A histogram or bar graph would be appropriate because they show the number

of times each item occurred. A circle graph would also be appropriate because it shows the percent of times each data value occurred.

Mid-Module Quiz (p. 1-30)

1. a. miles and hours; 55 mi/hr
b. dollars and pounds; $2.75/lb

2. a.

Cost of Cable Service

National		American
	2	8
9 9 7 2	3	2 5 7
6 4	4	6 6 8
8 4	5	1 4
4	6	

7 | 3 | means $37 | 3 | 5 means $35

b. Sample Response: Most of the packages for either company range from $30 to $60 per month. In general, American Cable seems to have the lower costs.
c. National: mean = $45.89, median = $44, mode = $39; American: mean = $41.89, median = $46, mode = $46

3. a. lower extreme = 32
b. upper extreme = 64
c. lower quartile = 38
d. upper quartile = 56

4.

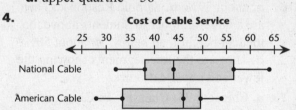

Cost of Cable Service

5. 35%

6. 25% of 20 = 5 classes are German or Russian

7. 40% of 360° = 144°

SECTION 3

Practice and Applications (p. 1-33)

1. B

2. Let c = total cost and n = the number of students; $c = 6n$.

3. Let i = the amount of interest and s = the amount of savings; $i = 0.05s$.

4. Let d = distance and h = the number of hours; $\frac{d}{50} = h$.

5. Let c = circumference and d = diameter; $c = 3d$.

6. No.

7. Yes.

8. Yes.

9. No.

10. Yes.

11. No.

12. 22

13. 4

14. 12

15. 12

16. $\frac{17}{3}$

17. 22

18. $\frac{17}{2}$

19. 54

20. 80

21. $h = 0.55(220 - a)$; about 102 beats per minute

22. x^2 and $5x^2$

23. $5x + 8$

24. no like terms

25. $4x$

26. no like terms

27. $5t + 16$

28. $7x^2 + 8x$

29. $11xy^2$

30. $20x + 6$

31. 12

32. 48 cm

33. **a.** $(12 + 2x)$ cm **b.** $(32 + 2x)$ cm

34. **a.** 30 cm **b.** 24 cm **c.** 20.25 cm

Study Guide Exercises (p. 1-38)

1. Let e = Theresa's earnings and let h = the number of hours she works: $e = 6.25h$.

2. Let c = the total cost of going to the zoo, let a = the number of adults, and let y = the number of children: $c = 4.50a + 2.50y$.

3. Let m = the total miles of the road trip and let h = the approximate number of hours the trip will take: $\frac{m}{60} = h$.

4. Let i = the number of people invited and let p = the number of potatoes Kevin needs: $2i = p$.

5. Let f = the total number of yards of fabric needed, let s = the number of shirts, and let d = the number of dresses: $2s + 3d = f$.

6. $m = 4$

7. $h = 8$

8. $y = 117$

9. $y = 8$

10. $p = 5$

11. $a = 3$

12. $m = 48$

13. $x = 27$

14. $t = 60$

15. $12m - 7$

16. $8 + 9ty - y$

17. no like terms

18. $x = 22$

19. $y = 3$

20. $t = 9$

21. $5h - 15$

Quick Quiz (p. 1-39)

1. Let c = the number of Calories you burn and let w = your weight: $c = 3.7w$.

2. Let s = the number of student tickets sold, let a = the number of adult tickets sold, and let m = total money collected: $m = 3s + 5a$.

3. $x = 168$

4. $y = 12$

5. $m = 7$

6. **a.** $10x + 8$ **b.** $17x^2 + 6$

SECTION 4

Practice and Applications (p. 1-43)

1. **a.** about 107 sec **b.** about 122 sec

2. **a.** about 1984–1996 **b.** women

3.

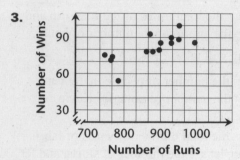

4. a. 247; 993; 746 **b.** Sample Response: Yes; Yes; The team that scores the most runs per game is the team that wins.

5. a. no pattern **b.** straight-line pattern

6. no correlation

7. negative correlation

8. a.

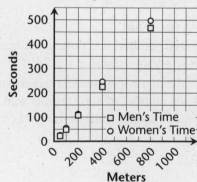

b. Sample Response: Yes; The number of wins increases as the number of runs increases. **c.** Sample Response: 100 wins

9. a. **Freestyle Record Times**

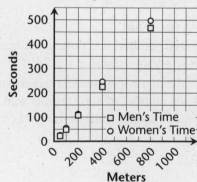

b. straight-line pattern

Freestyle Record Times

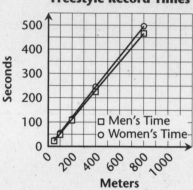

c. Sample Response: Their times increase at about the same rate.

Study Guide Exercises (p. 1-47)

1. Sample Response: about 87°

2. Sample Response: about 35

3.

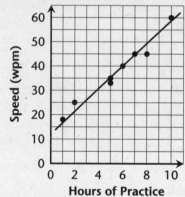

4. positive correlation

5. positive correlation

Quick Quiz (p. 1-48)

1–2.

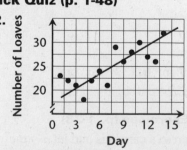

3. Sample Response: about 20 lb

4. no correlation

5. positive correlation

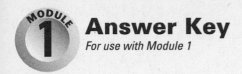

Answer Key

For use with Module 1

SECTION 5

Practice and Applications (p. 1-54)

1. **a.** Sample Response: Try a simpler problem. Divide the rectangle into equal sections, count the number of seedlings in one section, and multiply by the number of sections.
   b. Sample Response: Divide the garden into 12 equal sections; 72 seedlings.

2. **a.** Sample Response: Fill the 3 gal container; pour as much of the contents from the 3 gal container as you can into the 2 gal container; then pour the contents of the 2 gal container into the 5 gal container. Pour the remaining 1 gal in the 3 gal container into the 2 gal container. **b.** 2; Fill the 2 gal container; empty it into the 3 gal container; fill the 2 gal container again; fill the 3 gal container. One gal is left in the 2 gal container.
   c. Answers may vary.

3. **a.** Sample Response: The first number on the left is doubled each time, then add 4.
   b. $24 + 4 = 28$ **c.** 52 units
   d. $96 + 4 = 100; 100$

Study Guide Exercises (p. 1-56)

1. Sample Response: Use logical reasoning: Think of the 50 sit-ups as being separated into 5 equal groups (10 in each group). In 2 min, he can do what is represented by 2 of the 5 groups. So he can do 20 sit-ups in 2 min.

2. They will both play together for the first time on the 30th count. This will be the second note in the *eighth measure.*

3. **a–c.** Sample Responses are given.
   a. one 18-muffin tin and two 12-muffin tins
   b. one 12-muffin tin and five 6-muffin tins
   c. one 6-muffin tin and two 18-muffin tins

4. **a.** Check students' work.
   b. Sample Response:

Length	Width	Perimeter
1	20	42
2	10	24
4	5	18
5	4	18
10	2	24
20	1	42

c.

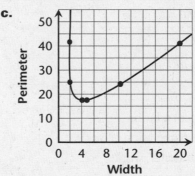

5. Answers will vary.

6. 2 units; Sample Response: $24 = 2(10) + 2w$; $w = 2$

Quick Quiz (p. 1-57)

1. **a.** Sample Response: Make an organized list of each possible pairing of 8 socks; for example: socks 1 and 2, socks 1 and 3, socks 1 and 4, and so on; 28 pairs. **b.** 12

2. 224 cm

END-OF-MODULE RESOURCES AND ASSESSMENTS

Practice and Applications, Sections 1–5 (p. 1-64)

1. not equivalent
2. equivalent
3. equivalent
4. equivalent
5. Sample Response: 40 times in 1 minute
6. 0.533 mi/min
7. $1.56/ft
8. 10%

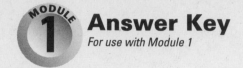

Answer Key
For use with Module 1

9. 234°
10. Check students' work; mean: $281\frac{1}{3}$; median: 270; mode 270; range: 145
11. 4; 31; 9
12. Sample Response: line graph; to show change over time
13. Sample Response: circle graph; to show parts of 100%
14. $x = 3$
15. $12x + 9$
16. $m^3 - m^2 + 5mn$
17. $3d + 3dr$
18. $x = 95$
19. $r = 100$
20. $y = 216$
21. positive correlation
22. negative correlation
23. Check students' work.
24. Sample Response:

Length	Width	Perimeter
1	30	62
2	15	34
3	10	26
5	6	22
6	5	22
10	3	26
15	2	34
30	1	62

25. Sample Response:

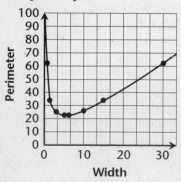

26. Answers will vary.
27. 5 units; Sample Response: $22 = 2(6) + 2w$; $w = 5$

Test Form A (p. 1-67)

1. **a.** 3 in. per day **b.** $1\frac{3}{4}$ ft per week **c.** 91 ft per year

2. **a.**

Base Cost of 1-day Rental

8-Wheelers		Rent-a-Truck
9 9 5 2 2	4	0 5 8 9 9 9
8 6	5	7
6	6	2 2 8 8
8 8 8 2	7	0

8 | 5 | means $58 | 6 | 2 means $62

b. Sample Response: In general, 8-Wheelers charges more for their trucks.

c. 8-Wheelers: mean = $59.42, median = $57, mode = $78
Rent-a-Truck: mean = $55.58, median = $53, mode = $49

3.

	Lower Extreme	Upper Extreme	Lower Quartile	Upper Quartile
8-Wheelers	$42	$78	$47	$75
Rent-a-Truck	$40	$70	$48.50	$65

4. **a.** The median cost of renting from Rent-a-Truck or 8-Wheelers is not significantly different, but the upper quartiles and upper extremes show that even Rent-a-Truck's highest priced rentals are cheaper than at least 25% of 8-Wheeler's rental prices.

b. The data are helpful to a new truck company because to compete, it can either undercut both of the other companies or offer trucks at a price between them.

5. 40% of 360° = 144°
6. **a.** histogram **b.** stem-and-leaf plot

7. a. and b.

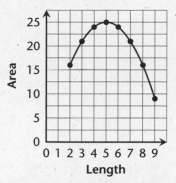

c. 5 in.

8. Sample Response: the amount of time a bowl of hot soup sits on the table and the temperature of the soup

9. a. $t = 3a + 2s + c$ where t = total cost, a = number of adult tickets, s = number of student tickets, and c = number of children's tickets. **b.** $13

10. a. unlike terms **b.** $7y$ **c.** $5r + 2rt$ **d.** $2gh$

11. a. $y = 3$ **b.** $x = 6$ **c.** $r = 12$ **d.** $h = 42$

Test Form B (p. 1-69)

1. a. 1.5 mi per min **b.** 7920 ft per min **c.** 132 ft per sec

2. a.

Base Cost of 1-day Rental

Power Cars		Ignition Rentals
7 7 6 4 2 2	2	5 5 5 9
2	3	6 6
4 4 4	4	2 2 4
2	5	5
5	6	5
	7	0

4 | 2 | means $24 | 4 | 2 means $42

b. Sample Response: In general, Power Cars charges less for their cars.

c. Power Cars: mean = $35.75, median = $29.50, mode = $44
Ignition Rentals: mean = $41.17, median = $39, mode = $25

3.

	Lower Extreme	Upper Extreme	Lower Quartile	Upper Quartile
Power Cars	$22	$65	$25	$44
Ignition Rentals	$25	$70	$27	$49.50

4. a. The lower quartile, median, and upper quartile for Power Cars are significantly lower than the corresponding values for Ignition Rentals, and 25% of the cars at Power Cars rent for less than any of the cars at Ignition Rentals.

b. The data are helpful to a new car rental company because to compete, it can either undercut both of the other companies or offer cars at a price between them.

5. 30% of 360° = 108°

6. a. stem-and-leaf plot **b.** histogram

7. a. and b.

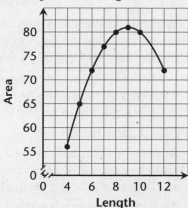

c. 9 cm

8. Sample Response: foot length and height

9. a. $t = 0.50c + 2.75p + 3s$ where t = total profit, c = number of candy bars, p = number of cans of popcorn, and s = number of T-shirts. **b.** $523.50

10. a. unlike terms **b.** $9y$ **c.** $7r + 5rt$ **d.** $9gh$

11. a. $y = 4.5$ **b.** $x = 5$ **c.** $y = 9$ **d.** $g = 32$

Standardized Test (p. 1-71)

1. c
2. b
3. a
4. d
5. a
6. c
7. a
8. c
9. b
10. d

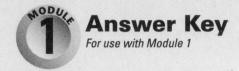

Answer Key

For use with Module 1

Performance Assessment (p. 1-72)

1. negative correlation

2. $A = \dfrac{3600}{h}$ (or $Ah = 3600$) where $A =$ the area of the base and $h =$ the height.

3. **a. and b.**

   a curved pattern

   Boxes with a Volume of 3600 cm³

   Area of Base (cm²) vs *Height (cm)*

4. Students' answers may vary, but they should state that the box top should be smaller than 10.5 cm by 24 cm; for example, 10 cm × 22 cm.

5. Answers will depend on the dimensions given in Exercise 4. For example, 10 cm × 22 cm gives an area of 220 cm².

6. Answers will depend on the dimensions given in Exercise 4. For example, for a base of 220 cm², the height would be about 16 cm.

7. Answers will depend on the dimensions given in Exercise 4. For example, with a base of 220 cm², the height is about 16.4 cm.

8. Answers may vary. Students should mention whether they used the height derived from the graph or the equation. For example, 10 cm × 22 cm × 16.4 cm gives a volume of 3608 cm³.

MODULE 2 Answer Key

For use with Module 2

MODULE 2

Diagnostic Test (p. 2-2)

1. 2
2. 38
3. 23
4. 72
5. −6
6. −24
7.

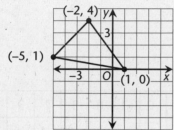

8. $-\frac{1}{6}$
9. $\frac{7}{5}$ or $1\frac{2}{5}$
10. $-\frac{47}{12}$ or $-3\frac{11}{12}$
11. $\frac{4}{9}$
12. a.

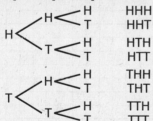

1st Flip	2nd Flip	3rd Flip	Outcomes
H	H	H	HHH
		T	HHT
	T	H	HTH
		T	HTT
T	H	H	THH
		T	THT
	T	H	TTH
		T	TTT

b. $\frac{1}{8}$

13. a. Midwestern teens; probably not, because the sample was taken from a particular region rather than the whole United States.

b. 472

14. Yes; how many hours a day do you think it is appropriate for children to watch TV?

15. a. about 278 girls   b. about 1130 boys

16. about 60%

17. about $45

SECTION 1

Practice and Applications (p. 2-13)

1. −31
2. 74
3. −7
4. 0
5. −85
6. −1
7. 14
8. 92
9. −104
10. −17
11. 18
12. −3
13. 14
14. 34
15. 1
16. 3
17. 41
18. 24
19. 13; −13
20. 17; −17
21. 4
22. 0
23. −6
24. 12 + (−8) + 5 + (−2); $7
25. Quadrant 3
26. $A(-4, -4)$; $B(-3, -2)$; $C(-2, -4)$
27. −3
28. −10
29. −5
30. 5
31. −16
32. −12
33. −3
34. 15
35. 17
36. 0
37. −21

38. 15

39. **a.** $S'(-8, 2)$; $H'(-5, 1)$; $A'(-3, 2)$; $P'(-4, 5)$; $E'(-7, 5)$ **b.** Sample Response: Add 5 to the *x*-coordinate and any integer to the *y*-coordinate.

40. −3

41. 2

42. 7

43. −4

44. 60

45. 184

46. 48

47. −128

48. 1536

49. 3

50. −8

51. −8

52. −32

53. 80

54. −16

55. 64

56. −56

57. 88

58. $t = 3(-4)$; −12°F

Study Guide Exercises (p. 2-18)

1. 12

2. 20

3. −6

4. −277

5. 45

6. 33

7. 2

8. 12

9. 8; −8

10. 4

11. −17

12. 22; −22

13. −22

14. 43

15. 50

16. −28

17. (7, 7)

18. $(x + 4, y + 3)$ and $(x - (-4), y - (-3))$

19. 18

20. −72

21. −56

22. 210

23. 11

24. −4

25. −9

26. 22

27. **a.**

x	−4	−3	−2	−1	0	1	2	3	4
y	8	6	4	2	0	−2	−4	−6	−8

b. $y = -2x$

c.

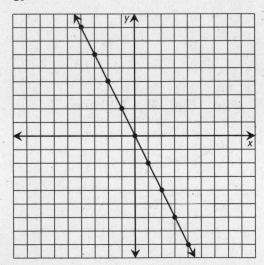

Quick Quiz (p. 2-19)

1. 9

2. 56

3. 14

4. 42

5. −12

6. −72

SECTION 2

Practice and Applications (p. 2-22)

1. $-1\frac{3}{8}$

2. $\frac{1}{3}$

3. $\frac{53}{63}$

4. $\frac{7}{12}$

5. -1

6. $1\frac{1}{5}$

7. $-1\frac{1}{3}$

8. $\frac{2}{5}$

9. $-1\frac{1}{24}$

10. $5\frac{3}{20}$

11. $7\frac{17}{18}$

12. $4\frac{4}{15}$

13. $4\frac{3}{10}$

14. $12\frac{1}{8}$

15. $6\frac{7}{24}$

16. $12\frac{9}{16}$

17. $5\frac{7}{8}$

18. $1\frac{7}{10}$

19. **a.** $16\frac{3}{4}$ lb **b.** Yes.

20. $-1\frac{2}{5}$

21. $1\frac{1}{8}$

22. $\frac{1}{5}$

23. $\frac{9}{16}$

24. $-1\frac{8}{9}$

25. $-\frac{1}{9}$

26. $-\frac{13}{15}$

27. $-\frac{4}{9}$

28. $-\frac{1}{6}$

29. $-\frac{101}{72}$ or $-1\frac{29}{72}$

30. $-\frac{1}{10}$

31. $-\frac{8}{15}$

32. $-\frac{3}{10}$

33. $\frac{1}{9}$

34. $-\frac{1}{6}$

35. $-\frac{1}{2}$

36. $2\frac{7}{8}$

37. $-7\frac{1}{8}$

38. $\frac{23}{24}$

39. $-7\frac{17}{20}$

40. $8\frac{3}{4}$

41. $-6\frac{1}{2}$

42. $12\frac{17}{20}$

43. $-4\frac{7}{18}$

44. $n = -5\frac{1}{6}$

45. $n = -1\frac{1}{6}$

46. **a.** $1\frac{1}{6}$ c **b.** No. **c.** $\frac{2}{6} = \frac{1}{3}$ c

Study Guide Exercises (p. 2-27)

1. $\frac{1}{16}$

2. $2\frac{3}{8}$

3. $-1\frac{1}{12}$

4. -1

5. $-1\frac{11}{20}$

6. $3\frac{7}{12}$

7. $-\frac{1}{12}$

8. $-\frac{2}{15}$

9. $-\frac{5}{9}$

10. 0

11. $-\frac{1}{30}$

12. $-\frac{1}{2}$

13. $-1\frac{1}{9}$

14. $1\frac{1}{2}$

15. $1\frac{13}{15}$

16. $5\frac{1}{2}$

17. $3\frac{2}{9}$

18. $-3\frac{17}{18}$

19. **a.** $\frac{9}{2}-\left(-\frac{8}{4}\right)=6\frac{1}{2}$ **b.** $-\frac{4}{8}-\left(-\frac{9}{2}\right)=4$

Quick Quiz (p. 2-28)

1. $-\frac{7}{8}$

2. $\frac{2}{15}$

3. $-\frac{7}{20}$

4. $5\frac{5}{6}$

5. $2\frac{17}{24}$

6. $-\frac{46}{63}$

Mid-Module Quiz (p. 2-29)

1. -15

2. 121

3. 21

4. -13

5. $y = -36$

6. $y = 54$

7. $y = -4$

8. $6 + (-13)$

9. $-3 + (-94)$

10. $-13 + 27$

11. $18 + 102$

12.

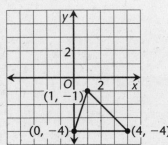

13. $-\frac{37}{28}$ or $-1\frac{9}{28}$

14. $\frac{125}{36}$ or $3\frac{17}{36}$

15. $\frac{7}{24}$

16. $\frac{13}{15}$

SECTION 3

Practice and Applications (p. 2-34)

1. not equally likely

2. not equally likely

3. equally likely

4. **a.** Check students' work. **b.** $\frac{1}{4}, \frac{1}{4}, \frac{1}{4}, \frac{1}{4}$
   c. Answers may vary.

5. $\frac{1}{6}$;

6. 0;

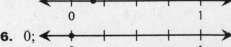

7. $\frac{1}{2}$;

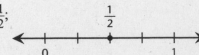

8. $\frac{1}{2}$;

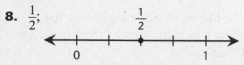

9. none; the probability of rolling an eight

10. **a.** $\frac{2}{5}$; $\frac{3}{5}$ **b.** $\frac{19}{49}$ **c.** $\frac{20}{49}$ **d.** dependent, because the first draw affects the second draw **e.** $\frac{20}{50}$; higher because of replacement

11. Sample Response:

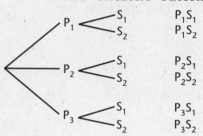

Pants	Sweaters	Outcome
P_1	S_1	P_1S_1
	S_2	P_1S_2
P_2	S_1	P_2S_1
	S_2	P_2S_2
P_3	S_1	P_3S_1
	S_2	P_3S_2

12. **a.** $\frac{1}{6}$ **b.** $\frac{1}{3}$

13.

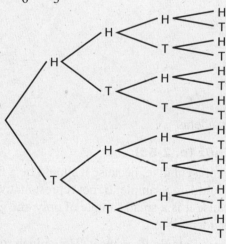

Study Guide Exercises (p. 2-38)

1. $\frac{18}{30}$ or $\frac{3}{5}$

2. Yes.

3. No.

4. $\frac{1}{5}$

5. $\frac{2}{5}$

6. 0

7. $\frac{3}{5}$

8. **a.** $\frac{10}{20}$ or $\frac{1}{2}$; $\frac{16}{20}$ or $\frac{4}{5}$ **b.** dependent; There are both fewer pencils as well as fewer *blue* pencils available for the second drawing, so the probability of drawing a blue pencil in event 2 depends on event 1.

9. **a.**

First spin	Second spin	Outcome
1	1	1, 1
	2	1, 2
	3	1, 3
2	1	2, 1
	2	2, 2
	3	2, 3
3	1	3, 1
	2	3, 2
	3	3, 3

b. 9 **c.** (1, 3), (2, 2), and (3, 1)

Quick Quiz (p. 2-39)

1. $\frac{1}{2}$

2. $\frac{1}{6}$

3. $\frac{4}{19}$

4. $\frac{1}{8}$

SECTION 4

Practice and Applications (p. 2-48)

1. biased; Sample Response: Which sport would you prefer, football or field hockey?

2. not biased

3. biased; Sample Response: Do you like action films or dramas?

4. not biased

5. Yes; Sample Response: because the money viewers spend on films is a good indicator of their preferences

6. No; Sample Response: Dark green is the most popular color, but only 30% chose it.

7. **a.** population: middle school students; sample: eighth grade students
b. No; students not in eighth grade are not represented.

8. **a.** 45.8% **b.** 33.3% **c.** 12.5%

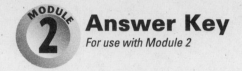
9. about 100; used the nearest fraction, $\frac{1}{4}$

10. 110; 56% is a little more than halfway between 50% and 60%.

11. 90; used multiples of 10%

12. **a.** Sample estimate: 440; actual: 449.6
    b. Sample estimate: 80; actual 96

13. **a.** 267 **b.** 270.4 **c.** 270.4
    d. Answers may vary.

14. 61.2

15. 161

16. 100.8

17. 268.32

18. 32

19. 13.8

20. Sample Response: The Elton John/Billy Joel concert grossed about 15.9% of the Stones' concert.

21. 54

22. 0.16

23. 20%

24. 2%

25. 70

26. 24

27. 150%

28. 300

29. **a.** $10 = 0.2x$; 50 **b.** Yes. Sample Response: There was a higher than average number of customers. **c.** Yes. Sample Response: The restaurant normally made $21 \times 28 = \$588$; during the promotion it made $40 \times \$21 = \$840$; $840 - free meals costing (10 \times \$15)$ or $\$150 = \$690$.

Study Guide Exercises (p. 2-54)

1. Yes; who would make the better class president, Kelly or Rachel?

2. Yes; should students use a pen or pencil to do their math homework?

3. No.

4. **a.** all babies; the babies whose parents received a survey, completed it, and sent it back to the company **b.** Sample Response:

No; the babies of parents who buy the company's food may not be representative of all babies.

5–10. Sample Responses are given.

5. about 300; "nice" fraction

6. about 100; multiples of 10%

7. about $7.40; multiples of 10%

8. about 3000; "nice" fraction

9. about $210; multiples of 10%

10. about 420; "nice" fraction

11. 216

12. 39.2

13. 11.1

14. 84

15. 45

16. 438

17. 7.6

18. 50

19. 360%

20. 94.5

21. 360

22. 50%

23. 20

24. 39 students

Quick Quiz (p. 2-55)

1. **a.** representative, because it should be a fairly random large sample **b.** not representative, because it is a small sample of only one grade of students

2. biased; Sample Response: "How much time should athletes spend practicing sports and how much time should they spend studying?"

3. about 300; Sample Response: Find one-fourth of 400 and multiply by 3.

4. 119

5. 57.6

6. 137.5

7. 12.5%

Answer Key

For use with Module 2

SECTION 5

Practice and Applications (p. 2-58)

1. $20; Sample Response: estimation and equivalent fraction

2. estimate: 40; actual: 39.6

3. estimate: 30; actual: 28.8

4. estimate: 70; actual: 63

5. estimate: 100; actual: 102.5

6. estimate: 46; actual: 43.7

7. estimate: 100; actual: 98

8. Yes; mental math gives $25 as 50% off, and $26 would be slightly less than 50% off.

9. Yes; mental math gives $18 as 25% off and $36 as 50% off, and $22 off is between $18 off and $36 off.

10. Yes; estimation gives $20 as 25% off.

11. Yes; mental math gives the discount range to be a price of $60 to $90. This price falls within that range.

12. Yes; mental math gives the discount range to be a price of $45 to $67.50. This price falls within that range.

13. No; by estimation; this price is more than 50% off, which is not within the range.

14. **a.** about $8850 **b.** about $9560 **c.** $8854.92; $9563.31 **d.** No; Sample Response: 8% of 8853 is greater than 8% of 8199.

15. **a.** Sample Response: about $\frac{1}{30}$ (1000 ÷ 30,000), or about 3.3%

    b. about 2.3%; Sample Response: The estimate is close.

16. **a.** Sample Response: about 16% $\left(\frac{1}{6} \text{ of } 100 \right)$

    b. 20%; Sample Response: The estimate is close.

17. **a.** about 12.2% **b.** about 11.5%

Study Guide Exercises (p. 2-62)

1. Sample Response: Change 73% to the "nice" fraction $\frac{3}{4}$, then find $\frac{3}{4}$ of $150; find 10% of $150, then multiply by 7.

2. about 18; 17.64

3. about 60; 57

4. about 8; 7.8

5. about 6; 4.88

6. about 20; 14.72

7. about 15; 11.7

8. about 180; 182.45

9. about 12; 12.32

10. $6; $24

11. $22.50; $52.50

12. $6; $9

13. 55%

14. 150%

15. 200%

16. 43.75%

17. 20.27%

18. 7.87%

19. 19.74%

Quick Quiz (p. 2-63)

1. Sample Response: about 63; 61.6

2. No; By estimation, it appears to be close, since half of $40 is $20, and using 10% to find 40% I get $16 off, which would be $40 – $16 = $24. However, using the formula for percent of decrease, the actual discount is only 35%.

3. **a.** 411% **b.** 80% **c.** Sample Response: Since 1975, the number of softball teams has increased. In the first 15 years there was a 411% increase. Overall, from 1975 to 1999, there has been an 822% increase in the number of softball teams for youth.

END-OF-MODULE RESOURCES AND ASSESSMENTS

Practice and Applications, Sections 1–5 (p. 2-64)

1. 12

2. 95

3. −8

4. −34

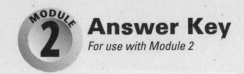

5. −5, 5

6. −12, 12

7. −22

8. 3

9. **a.** $A(1, 3)$; $B(−4, −1)$; $C(3, −1)$
   b. $A'(0, 5)$; $B'(−5, 1)$; $C'(2, 1)$

10. $−1\frac{1}{3}$

11. $1\frac{11}{60}$

12. $−5\frac{5}{8}$

13. $−\frac{4}{5}$

14. $\frac{5}{8}$

15. $1\frac{31}{63}$

16. $\frac{3}{9}$ or $\frac{1}{3}$

17. $\frac{8}{9}$

18. $\frac{5}{7}$

19. **a.**

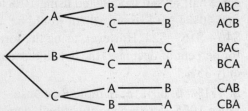

1st Student	2nd Student	3rd Student	Order of Students
A	B	C	ABC
A	C	B	ACB
B	A	C	BAC
B	C	A	BCA
C	A	B	CAB
C	B	A	CBA

   b. $\frac{3}{6}$ or $\frac{1}{2}$

20. 64.6

21. 6.75

22. 15.3

23. 45

24. 30

25. 87.6

26. 60

27. 1440

28. 350.46

29. 94.2%

30. 5.2

31. population: youths; sample: parents of youths

32. No; sample should be of the youths themselves.

33. Sample Response: about a 15% decrease

34. 25% increase

35. 40% decrease

36. 8% increase

Test Form A (p. 2-69)

1. 60

2. 14

3. −18

4. −96

5. 51

6. 2

7. −14

8. −21

9. 7 and −7

10. 12; Sample Response: Since −12 + 12 = 0, 12 and −12 are opposites.

11. Any two of the following: $(x + 3, y + (−6))$; $(x + 3, y − 6)$; $(x − (−3), y + (−6))$; $(x − (−3), y − 6)$

12. $−\frac{1}{8}$

13. $−\frac{41}{35}$ or $−1\frac{6}{35}$

14. $−\frac{7}{8}$

15. $−\frac{63}{10}$ or $−6\frac{3}{10}$

16.

```
        ┌── G
    R ──┼── B
        └── B
        ┌── R
    G ──┼── B
        └── B
        ┌── R
    B ──┼── G
        └── B
        ┌── R
    B ──┼── G
        └── B
```

17. $\frac{1}{6}$

18. $\frac{2}{5}$

19. No.

20. Sample Response: Survey people walking by the location between 8 A.M. and 10 A.M.

21. 74% of 850 = 629 girls

22. $\frac{350}{750}$ is a little less than $\frac{1}{2}$; about 45%.

23. The sale price is about 60% of $100 or $60.

24. Commercial lodgings decreased 5%; Park Service campgrounds decreased 22%; In back country lodging increased 18%.

Test Form B (p. 2-71)

1. 61
2. 17
3. −14
4. −84
5. 64
6. 5
7. −9
8. −10
9. 9 and −9
10. 15; Sample Response: Since −15 + 15 = 0, 15 and −15 are opposites.
11. Any two of the following: $(x − 2, y + 4)$; $(x + (−2), y + 4)$; $(x + (−2), y − (−4))$; $(x − 2, y − (−4))$
12. $\frac{2}{21}$
13. $-\frac{1}{40}$
14. $-\frac{5}{6}$
15. $-\frac{61}{10}$ or $-6\frac{1}{10}$
16.

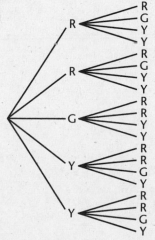

17. $\frac{1}{10}$

18. $\frac{17}{50}$

19. Yes; Sample Responses: Do diets provide adequate nutrition? How often do people diet?

20. Sample Response: Survey all the students in fourth period lunch.

21. 78% of x = 1320; $x ≈ 1692$ boys

22. $\frac{8.45}{6.50}$ is a little less than $\frac{8}{6} = 1\frac{1}{3} = 133\frac{1}{3}\%$; about 130%.

23. The sale price is about 70% of $80 or $56.

24. DVD spending is projected to increase 51%; Videocassette spending is projected to decrease 61%; Videogame spending is projected to increase 57%.

Standardized Test (p. 2-73)

1. c
2. b
3. d
4. c
5. c
6. d
7. b
8. c
9. c
10. a
11. b
12. a

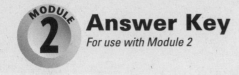

Answer Key
For use with Module 2

Performance Assessment (p. 2-74)

1.

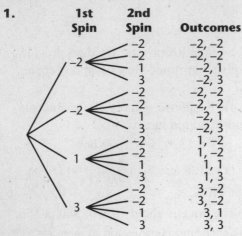

2. $P(-2, -2) = \dfrac{4}{16} = \dfrac{1}{4}$

3. $P(-2, 3) = \dfrac{2}{16} = \dfrac{1}{8}$

4. **Product of Two Spins**

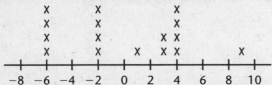

5. 50% of the products are greater than 0.

6. 75% of the products are greater than or equal to –2.

7. To get a product of –6, a player must spin (–2, 3) or (3, –2). $P((-2, 3)$ or $(3, -2)) = \dfrac{4}{16} = \dfrac{1}{4} = 25\%$.

25% of 12 turns = 3 turns. The player would expect to get a product of –6 on 3 of the 12 turns.

8. The sum of all 16 outcomes is 0, and all of the outcomes for a turn are equally likely, so this is a fair game.

Answer Key

For use after Modules 1 and 2

Modules 1 and 2 Cumulative Test (p. CT-1)

1. **a.** mean ≈ 45.7; median = 44.5; modes = 44 and 45 **b.** The mean; there are no gaps in the data or any unusually large or small data values that would affect the mean.

2. **a.**

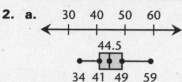

b. range = 25; lower extreme = 34; upper extreme = 59; lower quartile = 41; upper quartile = 49 **c.** 50%

3. **a. and c.**

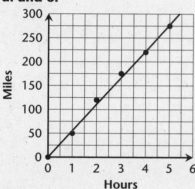

b. positive correlation **d.** about $7\frac{1}{2}$ hr

4. 40%

5. 40% of 30 = 12 classes

6. 10% of 360° = 36°

7.

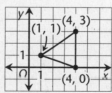

8. $x = 6$

9. $z = 32$

10. $x = 6$ or -6

11. $f^2 + f + 3$

12. 156 females voted

13. about 90%

14. **a.**

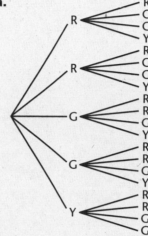

b. $\frac{1}{10}$

15. -6

16. -41

17. -6

18. -56

19. 12

20. -108

21. 14

22. 0

23.

24. $\frac{1}{6}$

25. $-\frac{19}{20}$

26. $\frac{11}{12}$